Webster's English to Romanian Crossword Puzzles: Level 1

Designed for ESL, ELP, EFL, TOEFL®, TOEIC® and AP® Learning

Webster's Online Dictionary
(www.websters-online-dictionary.org)

TOEFL®, TOEIC®, AP® and Advanced Placement® are trademarks of the Educational Testing Service which has neither reviewed nor endorsed this book.

Published by ICON Group International, Inc.
7404 Trade Street
San Diego, California 92121

www.icongrouponline.com

This edition published by ICON Classics in 2005
Printed in the United States of America.

Webster's Romanian – English Level 1 Crossword Puzzles adapted for ESL, ELP, EFL, TOEFL®, TOEIC® and AP®
Learning

The contents form this book have been extracted, with permission, from Webster's Online Dictionary, www.websters-online-dictionary.org (copyright Philip M. Parker, INSEAD).

ISBN 0-497-83175-9

PREFACE

Webster's Crossword Puzzles are edited for three audiences. The first audience consists of students who are actively building their vocabularies in either Romanian or English in order to take foreign service, translation certification, Advanced Placement® (AP®)[1] or similar examinations. By enjoying crossword puzzles, the reader can enrich their vocabulary in anticipation of an examination in either Romanian or English. The second includes Romanian-speaking students enrolled in an English Language Program (ELP), an English as a Foreign Language (EFL) program, an English as a Second Language Program (ESL), or in a TOEFL® or TOEIC® preparation program. The third audience includes English-speaking students enrolled in bilingual education programs or Romanian speakers enrolled in English speaking schools.

This edition is for Level 1 vocabulary, where the higher the level number, the more complicated the vocabulary. Though highly entertaining, if not addictive, this crossword puzzle book covers some 3000 translations. In this book, hints are in English, answers are in Romanian. This format is especially fun (or easiest) for people learning English; the format is most instructive, however, for people learning Romanian (i.e. the puzzles are a good challenge). Within each level, the puzzles are organized to expose players to shorter and more common words first. Subsequent puzzles mostly build on these using longer and more complicated vocabulary. Learning a language is always difficult. To ease the pain, hints are provided in small script at the bottom of each page, though these are selected to prevent an engineered solution to the puzzle. Players need to learn the meanings of the words in order to place them correctly. Full solutions are provided in the back of the book. These two features (hints and verifiable solutions), force the reader to decipher a word's meaning and serves to improve vocabulary retention and understanding. Translations are extracted from Webster's Online Dictionary. Further definitions of remaining terms as well as translations can be found at www.websters-online-dictionary.org. Enjoy!

The Editor
Webster's Online Dictionary
www.websters-online-dictionary.org

---

[1] TOEFL®, TOEIC®, AP® and Advanced Placement® are trademarks of the Educational Testing Service which has neither reviewed nor endorsed this book.

Puzzle #1:   Level 1 - Most Common

Across

2 good, nice
5 two
9 here
10 old
11 five
13 night
15 now
16 four
19 we
20 with
21 all, whole
22 year
23 he
25 not, no

Down

1 in, into, on
3 where
4 very, highly
6 money, dough
7 and
8 time
11 how
12 head
13 new
14 three
17 there
18 one
20 who
24 long

Solutions: acolo, Acum, aici, an, bani, bun, cap, cinci, Cine, Cu, Cum, doi, El, Foarte, în, lung, Noapte, Noi, nou, Nu, patru, şi, Timp, tot, trei, Unde, unu, vechi. (28 words). See www.websters-online-dictionary.org

Puzzle #2: Level 1 - Most Common

Across

2 from, of, by
3 water
5 this
8 man
10 on, upon
11 only, alone, solely
14 back
15 or
16 what
17 six
19 through
21 under, below, underneath
22 their
23 day
24 when

Down

1 government
2 yes, give, yea
3 other
4 which, what, who
6 you, ye
7 some
9 she
10 for
12 small, little
13 up
18 help, aid
20 nothing, naught, nought
25 but, gift

Solutions: acest, Ajutor, alt, apă, când, care, ce, Da, Dar, de, Ea, Guvern, lor, mic, nimic, nişte, numai, om, pe, Pentru, prin, şase, Sau, Spate, sub, sus, voi, Zi. (28 words). See www.websters-online-dictionary.org

Puzzle #3: Level 1 - Most Common

© Philip M. Parker, INSEAD; www.websters-online-dictionary.org

Across

4 left
8 many
11 have
12 our
13 down, downstairs
15 able, capable
17 hand
18 something
20 point, item
21 world
22 know
24 these
25 that
27 then

Down

1 work
2 about, on
3 if
5 group
6 well, boon
7 among, between
9 people
10 come
14 be
16 thing
17 much, umpteen
18 as
19 see
20 over
23 already, yet
26 at, to

Solutions: acel, aceste, Apoi, avea, bine, Ca, capabil, ceva, dacă, deja, despre, fi, funcţiona, Grup, între, jos, La, Lucru, lume, mână, mult, mulţi, noastre, oameni, Peste, Punct, stânga, şti, vedea, veni. (30 words). See www.websters-online-dictionary.org

Puzzle #4: Level 1 - Most Common

© Philip M. Parker, INSEAD; www.websters-online-dictionary.org

Across

7 development
8 affair, business
10 children
11 nevertheless, yet
12 school
14 far
16 frequently, often
17 name, appellation
18 woman
19 system
20 life
21 road, way
23 each
26 house
28 number

Down

1 different
2 right
3 although, though
4 council
5 fact
6 as, because, since
9 power
13 case
15 room
17 national
19 say
22 make
24 again
25 white
27 take

Solutions: adesea, afacere, alb, cameră, casă, caz, consiliu, Copii, deoarece, Departe, deşi, Dezvoltare, diferit, Dreapta, Drum, face, Fapt, femeie, Fiecare, iar, lua, naţional, numằr, Nume, Putere, şcoală, sistem, spune, totuşi, viaţă. (30 words). See www.websters-online-dictionary.org

Puzzle #5:   Level 1 - Most Common

© Philip M. Parker, INSEAD; www.websters-online-dictionary.org

Across

1 north
6 always, ever
7 free
8 war
9 voice
12 father
13 today
15 love, affection
16 ten
21 car
22 among
23 south
25 available
26 certain, sure
27 order
28 full, replete
29 open, light
30 mother

Down

2 round
3 million
4 question
5 law
10 book
11 black
14 court
17 body, corps
18 view
19 child
20 above, over
24 death

Solutions: azi, carte, copil, Corp, Deasupra, deschis, disponibil, Dragoste, întrebare, Lege, Liber, mamă, Milion, Moarte, Negru, nord, ordine, plin, Printre, război, rotund, sigur, sud, tată, totdeauna, Tribunal, vagon, Vedere, voce, zece. (30 words). See www.websters-online-dictionary.org

Puzzle #6: Level 1 - Very Common

© Philip M. Parker, INSEAD; www.websters-online-dictionary.org

Across

1 someone, anyone, somebody
4 friend, pal
6 eight
9 west
10 outcome, result
12 future, prospective
14 air
15 almost, near, nearly
17 century
19 bed, stalemate
20 felt
22 run
24 early
25 therefore
27 read
28 yesterday

Down

2 authority
3 try
5 history
7 price
8 wife
11 language, tongue
13 seven
16 so, thus
18 city, town
19 strong, forceful, potent
20 kind, sort
21 sometimes
23 east
26 herself, themselves

Solutions: Aer, alerga, Aproape, aşa, Autoritate, cineva, citi, deci, Devreme, est, fel, fetru, Ieri, încerca, Istorie, limbă, opt, oraş, pat, preţ, Prieten, puternic, rezultat, şapte, se, secol, soţie, uneori, vest, viitor. (30 words). See www.websters-online-dictionary.org

Puzzle #7: Level 1 - Very Common

Across

1 word
4 music
5 meeting
6 short, brief
7 quality
9 call
10 adage, saying
12 village
13 big, sea, large
15 fish
17 son, boy
20 play
21 ask
22 committee
23 fire
25 certainly
26 red
27 close
28 role

Down

2 understand
3 hospital
4 move
8 common
11 king
14 bring
16 hundred
18 tax
19 value
24 game
25 hard

© Philip M. Parker, INSEAD; www.websters-online-dictionary.org

Solutions: aduce, Calitate, chema, comitet, cuvînt, desigur, dur, fiu, foc, impozit, închide, întâlnire, înţelege, întreba, islaz, joc, juca, mare, mişca, muzică, peşte, proverb, rege, rol, roşu, Sat, scurt, spital, sută, valoare. (30 words). See www.websters-online-dictionary.org

Puzzle #8: Level 1 - Very Common

© Philip M. Parker, INSEAD; www.websters-online-dictionary.org

Across

1 hair
4 field
7 hear
8 royal
9 light
12 heart
13 thousand
14 park
17 account
20 stop
22 lead
23 letter
24 husband
25 lost
26 below

Down

1 maybe, perhaps
2 rose
3 subject
4 technology
5 space
6 basis
10 oil
11 art
15 chapter
16 speak, talk
18 force
19 happy, fortunate
21 risk
22 wall
24 advice, counsel

Solutions: artă, auzi, capitol, cont, Dedesubt, fericit, forţa, fundament, inimă, lumină, Mie, oprire, păr, parc, perete, pierdut, plumb, poate, regal, risc, scrisoare, sfat, soţ, spaţiu, subiect, tehnologie, Teren, trandafir, Ulei, vorbi. (30 words). See www.websters-online-dictionary.org

Puzzle #9:   Level 1 - Very Common

© Philip M. Parker, INSEAD; www.websters-online-dictionary.org

Across

3 Friday
5 tea
7 hour
10 blood
11 green
13 hold
14 sound
15 thank
20 county
21 beginning
23 Monday
25 storey, story
26 sun
27 anyway
28 heavy, hard, laborious
29 straight, right, law

Down

1 nor
2 amount
4 floor
6 attention
8 science
9 wrong
10 write
12 unit
16 human
17 theory
18 helpful, useful
19 hall
22 loss
24 easy, light

Solutions: atenţie, cantitate, Ceai, comitat, drept, element, etaj, greşit, greu, Hol, început, luni, mulţumi, nici, oră, oricum, pierdere, Podea, sânge, scrie, soare, ştiinţă, sunet, teorie, ţine, uman, uşor, util, verde, vineri. (30 words). See www.websters-online-dictionary.org

Puzzle #10:   Level 1 - Very Common

© Philip M. Parker, INSEAD; www.websters-online-dictionary.org

Across

3 football, soccer
6 chair
7 cold, bleak, frigid
8 glass
9 tree
12 bridge
18 twelve

19 newspaper, gazette, journal
20 ball
22 forty
24 warm
25 thirty
26 train
27 leg, foot

Down

1 brother
2 star
3 beautiful, fair, lovely
4 horse, knight
5 equipment, kit
8 rain
10 bus
11 coffee

13 eye
14 bear
15 wood
16 fifty
17 arm
21 wine
22 skin, leather
23 dry, arid

Solutions: autobuz, braț, cafea, cal, cald, Cincizeci, copac, Doisprezece, ECHIPAMENT, fotbal, frate, frumos, lemn, minge, ochi, Pahar, patruzeci, picior, piele, ploaie, pod, rece, Scaun, stea, treizeci, tren, urs, uscat, vin, ziar. (30 words). See www.websters-online-dictionary.org

Puzzle #11:   Level 1 - Somewhat Common

Across

3 sleep
6 audience
7 forest
10 blue
13 brown
14 slowly
15 studio, workshop
16 ring
17 museum
18 quarter
20 wind
23 weight
24 gold
26 key
28 engine
30 pain, ache

Down

1 fifteen
2 rich, wealthy, plentiful
4 stone, rock
5 drink
8 male
9 mouth
11 weather, time
12 correct
19 hot
21 box
22 wide
25 expensive, dear
27 dog
29 river

Solutions: albastru, atelier, aur, bea, bogat, câine, cheie, Cincisprezece, corect, Cutie, dormi, durere, fierbinte, Greutate, gură, încet, Inel, larg, maro, Masculin, motor, Muzeu, pădure, piatră, public, râu, scump, Sfert, vânt, Vreme. (30 words). See www.websters-online-dictionary.org

Puzzle #12: Level 1 - Somewhat Common

© Philip M. Parker, INSEAD; www.websters-online-dictionary.org

Across

2 goal, aim, purpose
5 seat, place, spot
8 nobody, anyone
10 Sunday
11 daughter
12 speaker
13 birth
14 effective
17 soft
18 alone, only, solely
22 degree
23 sit
25 statement
26 empty, void
27 peace

Down

1 danger
3 walk
4 change, exchange
6 middle, waist
7 western
9 thin
13 trouble
15 clean, cleanly
16 fast
17 tomorrow
19 ready
20 physical
21 hill
22 neck
24 attack

Solutions: Atac, curat, Deal, declarație, Duminică, eficace, fiică, fizic, gât, gata, gol, grad, Loc, mâine, Mijloc, Moale, naştere, necaz, nimeni, occidental, pace, Pericol, plimba, Repede, schimb, scop, şedea, singur, subţire, vorbitor. (30 words). See www.websters-online-dictionary.org

Puzzle #13: Level 1 - Somewhat Common

© Philip M. Parker, INSEAD; www.websters-online-dictionary.org

Across

4 married
5 kitchen
8 begin
9 daily
10 blacksmith, smith
11 corner
17 mark, sign
18 insurance
19 debate
23 clothes
25 kingdom
26 technical
27 meaning
28 budget
29 message

Down

1 additional
2 gas
3 crime
5 check
6 prison
7 dear
12 length
13 match
14 possibility
15 somewhere
16 truth
20 impact
21 average
22 send
24 fear

Solutions: adevăr, asigurare, bon, bucătărie, Buget, chibrit, ciocnire, colţ, conjugal, Delict, dezbatere, drag, fierar, frică, gaz, haine, începe, închisoare, lungime, Medie, Mesaj, posibilitate, regat, semn, sens, suplimentar, tehnic, trimite, undeva, zilnic. (30 words). See www.websters-online-dictionary.org

Puzzle #14: Level 1 - Somewhat Common

© Philip M. Parker, INSEAD; www.websters-online-dictionary.org

Across

2 sentence
3 historian, historical
6 pair
8 unemployment
11 ample, sufficient
13 quiet
14 southern
15 background
16 copy
18 equal
20 driver
21 forget
24 object, thing
26 thanks
28 travel
29 felicitous, seemly, suitable

Down

1 source, spring
4 gain, profit
5 dangerous
7 safe
9 elsewhere
10 patient
12 bottom
17 mental
19 belief
22 usual
23 package
25 jack
26 die
27 hell

Solutions: aiurea, călătorie, câştig, colet, credinţă, cric, egal, exemplar, fond, Fund, iad, istoric, izvor, liniştit, mintal, mulţumiri, muri, obiect, obişnuit, pacient, pereche, periculos, potrivit, propoziţie, seif, şofer, şomaj, sudic, suficient, uita. (30 words). See www.websters-online-dictionary.org

Puzzle #15:   Level 1 - Somewhat Common

© Philip M. Parker, INSEAD; www.websters-online-dictionary.org

Across

1 smoke
5 lake
6 nose
8 airport
10 ear
11 knee
14 mountain
15 Thursday
17 tent
19 ticket
20 bone
21 milk
23 salt
25 owner
26 yellow
28 egg

Down

1 liver
2 flower, bloom, blossom
3 Wednesday
4 coal
7 chest, breast, bosom
9 rice
12 sky, heaven
13 narrow
16 eighty
17 meat
18 sand
22 pig, hog, swine
24 beer, ale
27 lion

Solutions: aeroport, bere, bilet, cărbune, Carne, Cer, cort, ficat, floare, fum, galben, genunchi, îngust, joi, lac, lapte, leu, miercuri, munte, nas, nisip, optzeci, orez, os, ou, piept, porc, proprietar, sare, ureche. (30 words). See www.websters-online-dictionary.org

Puzzle #16: Level 1 - Common

© Philip M. Parker, INSEAD; www.websters-online-dictionary.org

Across

5 dirty, messy, smutty
8 silver
9 clock, watch
10 dress
12 snake, serpent
14 eighteen
15 butter
16 bedroom
17 pencil
22 iron
23 garlic
25 oxygen
27 cloud
28 eleven

Down

1 cemetery, churchyard, graveyard
2 butterfly
3 luggage, baggage
4 eagle, vulture
6 envelope
7 valley
9 waiter
11 rabbit
13 pocket
16 tooth
18 elephant
19 fox, vixen
20 author, writer
21 desk, office, bureau
24 tiger
26 sheep

Solutions: argint, autor, bagaj, Birou, buzunar, ceas, chelner, cimitir, creion, dinte, dormitor, elefant, fier, fluture, iepure, murdar, nor, Oaie, Optsprezece, oxigen, plic, rochie, şarpe, tigru, Unsprezece, unt, usturoi, vale, vulpe, vultur. (30 words).
See www.websters-online-dictionary.org

Puzzle #17:   Level 1 - Common

Across

2 cattle
7 sick, ill, unwell
8 dust, powder
10 tennis
11 cheek
13 thirteen
17 moon, month
18 sweet
19 snow
21 fishing
24 smooth
26 tower
27 thick
28 fruit
29 uncle

Down

1 weak, light, thin
3 grass
4 bath, bathroom
5 arrival
6 fourteen
9 coat
11 glasses, spectacles
12 wave
14 entrance, admittance
15 chemistry
16 circle, hoop
20 departure
22 mouse
23 wet
25 sharp

Solutions: ascuţit, Baie, bolnav, cerc, chimie, dulce, fruct, gros, iarbă, intrare, lună, neted, obraz, ochelari, Paisprezece, palton, pescuit, plecare, praf, slab, şoarece, sosire, tenis, treisprezece, Turn, ud, unchi, val, Vite, zăpadă. (30 words). See www.websters-online-dictionary.org

Puzzle #18: Level 1 - Common

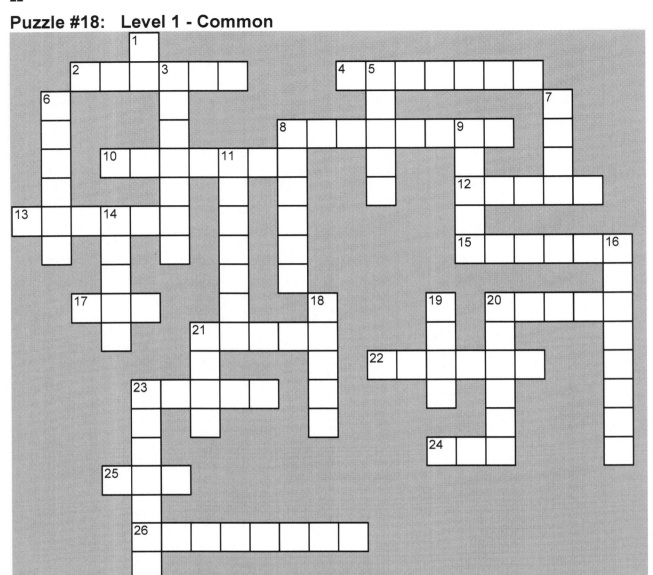

© Philip M. Parker, INSEAD; www.websters-online-dictionary.org

Across

2 forehead
4 velvet
8 triangle
10 battery
12 menu
13 barn, granary
15 bat, lilac
17 elbow, ell
20 pepper
21 honey
22 potato
23 flag
24 wolf
25 boxing
26 architect

Down

1 thou, you
3 button
5 advertisement, announcement
6 hammer
7 glue
8 theater, theatre, playhouse
9 porter
11 kidney
14 barrel
16 rainbow
18 nephew, grandson
19 deer, stag
20 towel
21 lamb
23 rat

Solutions: anunț, arhitect, baterie, box, Butoi, Cartof, Catifea, cerb, ciocan, Clei, cot, curcubeu, frunte, hamal, Hambar, liliac, lup, meniu, miel, miere, nasture, nepot, piper, Prosop, rinichi, șobolan, steag, teatru, triunghi, tu. (30 words). See www.websters-online-dictionary.org

Puzzle #19: Level 1 - Common

© Philip M. Parker, INSEAD; www.websters-online-dictionary.org

Across

3 tired
5 gallery
7 sugar
9 musical
10 drawing
11 bishop, crazy, insane
14 noise
15 shop, store
17 cheap, inexpensive
19 paint
21 landscape
23 photograph
25 customer
26 philosophy
27 throw

Down

1 bird
2 smell
4 painting
6 comfort
8 wing
9 Tuesday
12 crew
13 dance
16 brain
18 gift
20 finger
21 platform
22 deaf
24 cat
25 courtyard, yard, court

Puzzle #20: Level 1 - Common

© Philip M. Parker, INSEAD; www.websters-online-dictionary.org

Across

3 engineer
5 pen
9 passenger
10 salmon
11 counter
14 priest, minister, parson
15 courage, bravery, grit
18 farmer
19 tourist
20 belt
21 movie
22 brush
25 pan
26 psychology
28 rope
29 baker

Down

1 trousers, pants
2 fat
4 dollar
6 tail
7 illegal, unlawful
8 crystal
12 happiness, felicity
13 grandfather
16 burn
17 dictionary
19 waist
23 remainder, remnant
24 colleague
27 chaos

Solutions: arde, brutar, bunic, coadă, coleg, Cristal, curaj, Curea, dicționar, dolar, fericire, fermier, film, Funie, grăsime, haos, ilegal, inginer, pantaloni, Pasager, perie, Preot, psihologie, rest, Somon, talie, tejghea, Tigaie, toc, turist. (30 words). See
www.websters-online-dictionary.org

Puzzle #21: Level 1 - Not Very Common

© Philip M. Parker, INSEAD; www.websters-online-dictionary.org

Across

1 jealous
3 cow
5 skull
8 lobby, vestibule
10 oak
13 communism
15 vacuum
16 horn
17 fist
18 knight
19 thunder
21 custom, habit, way
23 photographer
25 tourism
27 divinity, theology
28 cylinder

Down

1 collar
2 librarian
4 oven
6 aquarium
7 corn, maize
9 ballet
11 hydrogen
12 hospitality
14 swim
17 shoe
20 threshold
22 basket
24 tobacco
26 juice

Solutions: Acvariu, Balet, bibliotecar, Cavaler, cilindru, comunism, corn, coş, craniu, Cuptor, fotograf, gelos, Guler, hidrogen, înota, Obicei, ospitalitate, pantof, Porumb, prag, pumn, stejar, suc, teologie, tunet, turism, tutun, vacă, vestibul, vid. (30 words). See www.websters-online-dictionary.org

Puzzle #22: Level 1 - Not Very Common

© Philip M. Parker, INSEAD; www.websters-online-dictionary.org

Across

6 calf
8 stool
9 dolphin
10 freeze
12 dragon
13 wallet
14 kite
16 barley
17 musician
20 seaside
21 skeleton
24 nylon
25 screen
27 guide
28 parcel
29 jockey

Down

1 catch
2 wonderful
3 lime
4 armchair
5 debt
7 cardboard
11 jealousy
15 physician
17 donkey
18 flight
19 archaeology
22 cough
23 bean
26 nail

Solutions: arheologie, Balaur, carton, Cui, datorie, delfin, ecran, fasole, fotoliu, gelozie, ghid, îngheţa, jocheu, litoral, măgar, medic, minunat, muzician, Nailon, orz, pachet, Portofel, prinde, schelet, Taburet, tuse, var, viţel, zbor, zmeu. (30 words). See www.websters-online-dictionary.org

Puzzle #23:   Level 1 - Not Very Common

© Philip M. Parker, INSEAD; www.websters-online-dictionary.org

Across

1 glad
5 extensive
6 approval
7 valuable
9 hole
10 somewhat
12 corridor, passage
14 culpable, culprit, guilty
15 sequence
17 fortunate, lucky
19 reader
20 cove, guy
23 engineering
26 maintenance
27 massive
28 dream

Down

2 subsequent
3 flat
4 lead, leadership
7 revenue
8 somehow
11 roof
13 file
16 youth
18 sixty
21 taste
22 flow
23 vast
24 unique
25 ourselves

Solutions: acoperiş, apartament, aprobare, bucuros, cam, cititor, conducere, coridor, cumva, curge, Dosar, gaură, gust, imens, individ, inginerie, întreţinere, masiv, ne, norocos, şaizeci, succesiune, Tineret, ulterior, unic, valoros, vast, venit, vinovat, vis. (30 words). See www.websters-online-dictionary.org

Puzzle #24: Level 1 - Not Very Common

Across

3 push
6 stick
8 aunt
9 duke
10 golden
11 empire
14 bell
16 enemy
17 chain
22 ice
24 equivalent
25 achievement
27 parish
28 idea, notion

Down

1 suggestion
2 namely, specifically
4 fly
5 visual
7 writer
9 trained
12 gruff, rough
13 dish, plate
15 chancellor
16 fault
18 defendant
19 decade
20 pollution
21 objective
23 rent
26 steel

Solutions: acuzat, anume, aspru, auriu, baston, cancelar, chirie, clopot, deceniu, defect, dresat, duce, duşman, echivalent, farfurie, gheaţă, idee, imperiu, împinge, lanţ, mătuşă, muscă, obiectiv, oţel, parohie, poluare, realizare, scriitor, sugestie, vizual. (30 words). See www.websters-online-dictionary.org

Puzzle #25: Level 1 - Not Very Common

Across

1 surgery
7 tank
9 kiss
10 barely
11 split
14 expert
16 seventy
18 plaintiff
19 jury
20 joy
21 wan
23 visible
25 mission
27 luck
29 register

Down

2 phrase
3 equation
4 mummy
5 communist
6 cruel, raw
8 shirt
12 sixteen
13 knife
15 ceiling
17 discovery
22 destruction
24 cotton
25 mechanism
26 poem, poetry
28 hate

Solutions: bucurie, bumbac, cămaşă, chirurgie, comunist, crud, cuţit, descoperire, despica, distrugere, doar, ecuaţie, expresie, înregistra, juriu, mecanism, misiune, mumie, noroc, palid, poezie, reclamant, şaisprezece, şaptezeci, sărut, specialist, Tanc, Tavan, urî, vizibil. (30 words). See www.websters-online-dictionary.org

Puzzle #26: Level 1 - Easy

© Philip M. Parker, INSEAD; www.websters-online-dictionary.org

Across

4 unfair
6 scientist
9 carpet
10 tin
11 hero
13 tissue
14 miller
16 addition
20 tunnel
21 unhappy
24 mystery
25 root
26 guardian, trustee
28 summary
29 anywhere, wherever

Down

1 anniversary
2 phenomenon
3 cheque
5 reception
7 barrister, lawyer
8 conviction
12 friendship
15 storm
17 withdrawal
18 lesson
19 cigarette
22 bitter
23 apple
24 witness
27 ford

Solutions: Adunare, amar, aniversare, avocat, cec, condamnare, cositor, covor, erou, fenomen, furtună, lecţie, măr, martor, mister, Morar, nedrept, nefericit, oriunde, prietenie, primire, rădăcină, retragere, rezumat, savant, ţesut, ţigară, tunel, tutore, Vad. (30 words). See www.websters-online-dictionary.org

Puzzle #27:   Level 1 - Easy

© Philip M. Parker, INSEAD; www.websters-online-dictionary.org

Across

2 seventeen
4 neighbour
5 correspondent
6 mayor
8 merchant
10 isolation
13 chronic
14 appendix
19 monthly
20 dull
21 resigned
22 fence
23 chicken
24 systematic
26 reign
27 lover
28 example, instance, lead

Down

1 forgiveness, pardon
2 symbol
3 therapy
5 chemical
7 scarcely
9 manufacturer
11 commander
12 cousin
15 equity
16 pipe, tube
17 suicide
18 abode, residence
25 bank, shore

Solutions: abia, apendice, bont, chimic, comandant, comerciant, corespondent, cronic, domiciliu, domnie, echitate, exemplu, fabricant, Gard, iertare, iubit, izolare, lunar, mal, primar, Pui, resemnat, şaptesprezece, simbol, sinucidere, sistematic, terapie, tub, văr, vecin. (30 words). See www.websters-online-dictionary.org

Puzzle #28: Level 1 - Easy

© Philip M. Parker, INSEAD; www.websters-online-dictionary.org

Across

1 forum
8 dynamic
11 prior
13 dean
14 lily
16 indefinite, vague
19 pond
24 super
26 tournament
27 racial
28 publisher
29 equilibrium

Down

2 hostile
3 orange
4 bull
5 liquid
6 myth
7 anyone, whoever
9 avenue
10 manor
12 seed
15 rejection
17 applicable
18 adviser
19 hierarchy
20 rhythm
21 eager
22 vessel
23 deck
25 hard, loud

Solutions: Alee, anterior, aplicabil, conac, consilier, Crin, Decan, dinamic, dornic, echilibru, editor, figurant, for, iaz, ierarhie, lichid, mit, oricine, ostil, portocală, punte, rasial, respingere, ritm, sămânţă, tare, Taur, turnir, vag, vas. (30 words). See www.websters-online-dictionary.org

Puzzle #29: Level 1 - Easy

© Philip M. Parker, INSEAD; www.websters-online-dictionary.org

Across

1 crude
3 shelf
6 archbishop
7 copper
10 equality
11 leaf
13 to, toward
14 inn
16 journalist
17 inherent
18 lorry
21 validity
22 eve
23 bloke
25 drunk
26 skilled
27 loyal
28 unacceptable

Down

2 terror
4 pavement
5 sovereignty
8 striker
9 butler
12 hostility
15 appreciation
19 unavailing,
   unnecessary, useless
20 honourable,
   respectable
24 curtain
25 dioxide
26 nest

Solutions: ajun, apreciere, arhiepiscop, beat, bioxid, brut, calificat, camion, Cuib, cupru, egalitate, frunză, grevist, han, inacceptabil, inerent, inutil, loial, Majordom, onorabil, ostilitate, perdea, Raft, spre, suveranitate, teroare, tip, trotuar, valabilitate, ziarist. (30 words). See www.websters-online-dictionary.org

Puzzle #30: Level 1 - Easy

© Philip M. Parker, INSEAD; www.websters-online-dictionary.org

Across

1 foolish
7 luxury
8 jazz
13 coherent
14 abortion
15 erosion
16 cheerful
20 stamp
23 bass
24 lid
25 hunger
27 throne
28 rod
30 territorial

Down

2 subjective
3 gravy, sauce
4 ash
5 fury
6 polytechnic
9 ferry
10 bile
11 sweat
12 shy
17 helicopter
18 orthodox
19 tenth
21 gradual
22 apparatus
26 cooper
29 needle

Solutions: Ac, aparat, avorton, bac, bas, Capac, coerent, Dogar, elicopter, eroziune, fiere, foame, frasin, furie, jaz, lux, ortodox, politehnic, prostesc, ruşinos, sos, subiectiv, teritorial, Timbru, transpiraţie, treptat, tron, vergea, voios, zecime. (30 words). See www.websters-online-dictionary.org

Puzzle #31:   Level 1 - Fairly Easy

© Philip M. Parker, INSEAD; www.websters-online-dictionary.org

Across

1 loving
5 stunning
6 trophy
8 noisy
10 couch, settee, sofa
13 artist, painter
15 presently
18 yacht
19 vivid
21 trainer
22 bad, poorly
24 graph
26 vocational
27 lieutenant
28 cage
29 methodology

Down

1 immune
2 exit
3 drawer
4 owl
7 folly
9 surgeon
11 against, versus
12 fog
14 immigration
16 optional
17 domain, realm
20 nuisance
23 choir, chorus
25 slice

Solutions: antrenor, bufniță, Canapea, ceață, chirurg, colivie, contra, cor, domeniu, facultativ, Felie, grafic, iaht, ieşire, imediat, imigrare, imun, iubitor, locotenent, metodologie, Nebunie, pacoste, pictor, profesional, prost, sertar, splendid, trofeu, viu, zgomotos. (30 words). See www.websters-online-dictionary.org

Puzzle #32: Level 1 - Fairly Easy

© Philip M. Parker, INSEAD; www.websters-online-dictionary.org

Across

1 ally
4 maid
5 rotten
8 recorder
10 lazy
13 asylum
15 imminent
16 accountant
17 frost
18 debtor
21 mankind
26 builder
27 surgical
28 bicycle
29 telly

Down

2 assertion
3 steal
5 feasible
6 ruler
7 trustee
9 whichever
11 highway
12 pine
14 squadron
19 amnesty
20 accompany
22 deadly
23 parking
24 corpse
25 reed

Solutions: administrator, afirmare, aliat, amnistie, bicicletă, cadavru, chirurgical, constructor, contabil, datornic, domnitor, escadron, fura, ger, iminent, însoţi, leneş, magnetofon, mortal, omenire, oricare, parcare, pin, posibil, putred, refugiu, servitoare, şosea, Stuf, televizor. (30 words). See www.websters-online-dictionary.org

Puzzle #33:   Level 1 - Fairly Easy

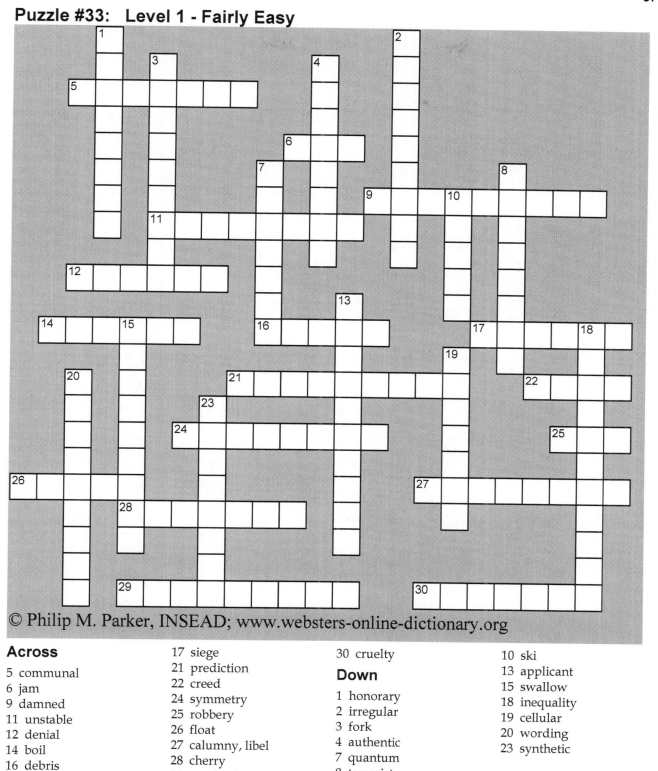

© Philip M. Parker, INSEAD; www.websters-online-dictionary.org

Across

5 communal
6 jam
9 damned
11 unstable
12 denial
14 boil
16 debris

17 siege
21 prediction
22 creed
24 symmetry
25 robbery
26 float
27 calumny, libel
28 cherry
29 notebook

30 cruelty

Down

1 honorary
2 irregular
3 fork
4 authentic
7 quantum
8 terrorist

10 ski
13 applicant
15 swallow
18 inequality
19 cellular
20 wording
23 synthetic

Solutions: asediu, autentic, blestemat, Blocnotes, calomnie, celular, cireaşă, comunal, crez, cruzime, cuantum, fierbe, formulare, furculiţă, Gem, inegalitate, instabil, jaf, moloz, negare, neregulat, onorific, pluti, prezicere, rândunică, schiu, simetrie, sintetic, solicitant, terorist. (30 words). See www.websters-online-dictionary.org

Puzzle #34:   Level 1 - Fairly Easy

© Philip M. Parker, INSEAD; www.websters-online-dictionary.org

Across

2 admiral
5 substantive
7 volcanic
10 desert, wilderness
14 hearsay, rumour
15 residual
17 impetus
19 rosemary
20 thief
21 balloon
22 acre, sour
23 terrorism
26 ax, axe
27 renowned
28 fussy, hectic, restless
29 onion
30 quotation

Down

1 pathetic
3 knot
4 pony
6 robust
8 gospel
9 mosaic
11 saddle
12 honesty
13 overseer,
   superintendent,
   supervisor
16 cement
18 passport
24 tomato
25 selfish

Solutions: acru, agitat, amiral, Balon, ceapă, ciment, cinste, citat, egoist, evanghelie, hoţ, impuls, independent, mozaic, nod, paşaport, patetic, ponei, pustiu, renumit, rezidual, roşie, Rozmarin, şa, supraveghetor, terorism, topor, viguros, vulcanic, zvon. (30 words). See www.websters-online-dictionary.org

Puzzle #35: Level 1 - Fairly Easy

© Philip M. Parker, INSEAD; www.websters-online-dictionary.org

Across

1 pitiless, ruthless
2 inner, inward
5 clinging
8 resistant
9 screw
11 anguish, ordeal
13 lightning
16 dusk
20 picturesque
21 theatrical
23 novelist
24 qualitative
25 readiness
26 jar
28 banker
29 anthropology

Down

1 nut
3 reservation
4 sensory
6 glossy
7 unofficial
10 sweater
12 immunity
14 cannon
15 authoritative
17 conquest
18 rub
19 donor
22 allegiance, obedience
27 ripe

Solutions: amurg, antropologie, autoritar, bancher, Borcan, calitativ, chin, colant, copt, cucerire, donator, freca, fulger, imunitate, interior, lucios, nemilos, neoficial, nucă, pitoresc, promptitudine, Pulover, Rezervare, rezistent, romancier, senzorial, supunere, şurub, teatral, tun. (30 words). See www.websters-online-dictionary.org

Puzzle #36:   Level 1 - Not So Easy

© Philip M. Parker, INSEAD; www.websters-online-dictionary.org

Across

4 suitcase
7 goat
8 juvenile, youthful
10 novelty
12 burglary
14 intricate
16 symptom
17 nomination
18 mole
19 bowling
21 translate
25 extinction
26 philosopher
28 heroic
29 tyre
30 outer, outside, outward

Down

1 humid, moist, wet
2 stylistic
3 dancer
5 dam
6 majesty
9 noun
11 advisable
13 proximity, vicinity
15 tedious
20 kindred, kinship
22 coupon
23 astonishment
24 hilarious, jaunty, jovial
27 potter

Solutions: aluniță, apropiere, Baraj, capră, complicat, cupon, dansator, eroic, exterior, filozof, geamantan, maiestate, noutate, numire, Olar, plicticos, pneu, Popice, recomandabil, rudenie, simptom, spargere, stilistic, stingere, substantiv, tineresc, traduce, uimire, umed, vesel. (30 words). See www.websters-online-dictionary.org

Puzzle #37: Level 1 - Not So Easy

© Philip M. Parker, INSEAD; www.websters-online-dictionary.org

Across

5 carrot
6 mast
7 charcoal
9 reef
11 plump
13 bark
17 fashionable, stylish
21 lucrative
23 exhaustion
25 worm
26 eccentric
27 cucumber
28 mattress
29 dessert

Down

1 refrigerator, fridge
2 rectangle
3 sailor, mariner
4 razor
8 alphabet
10 flute
12 pigeon, dove
13 sausage
14 applause
15 scissors, shears
16 comb
18 buffet
19 elevator
20 volcano
22 recurrence
24 luxurious

Solutions: Alfabet, aplauze, brici, bufet, castravete, catarg, Desert, dreptunghi, durduliu, elegant, epuizare, excentric, flaut, foarfece, frigider, lift, luxos, mangal, marinar, morcov, pieptene, porumbel, profitabil, Recif, repetare, salam, saltea, scoarță, vierme, vulcan. (30 words). See www.websters-online-dictionary.org

Puzzle #38:   Level 1 - Not So Easy

© Philip M. Parker, INSEAD; www.websters-online-dictionary.org

Across

1 bulb
4 chess
6 perfume
10 bouquet
11 vinegar
13 cocoa
14 pineapple
17 mythology
18 shark
19 cuckoo
20 snail
24 feather
25 physiology
26 rum
27 barber, hairdresser

Down

1 sponge
2 cone
3 symphony
4 symbolism
5 penguin
6 parrot
7 lipstick
8 ashes
9 fisherman
12 hockey
15 mosque
16 pedestrian
21 necklace
22 beech
23 buffalo

Solutions: ananas, bec, bivol, Buchet, burete, Cacao, colier, con, cuc, fag, fiziologie, frizer, Hochei, melc, mitologie, Moschee, oţet, pană, Papagal, parfum, pescar, Pieton, Pinguin, rechin, rom, Ruj, şah, scrum, simbolism, Simfonie. (30 words). See www.websters-online-dictionary.org

Puzzle #39:   Level 1 - Not So Easy

© Philip M. Parker, INSEAD; www.websters-online-dictionary.org

Across

3 willow
4 dynasty
8 garbage
10 hypothetical
11 solemn
13 pleasing
14 pawn
15 mortal
17 lighthouse, beacon
19 listener
20 massage
21 mute, dumb
23 beak
24 athletics
25 pupil, schoolboy
26 avoidance
28 gifted

Down

1 syrup
2 corporal
5 tsar
6 apprentice
7 contingency
9 swollen
12 camouflage
14 rainy
16 rucksack, knapsack
18 hedgehog
21 mass, multitude
22 messenger
27 thirst, thirsty

Solutions: agreabil, arici, atletism, auditor, Camuflaj, Caporal, Cioc, dinastie, elev, eventualitate, evitare, Far, grav, Gunoi, ipotetic, masaj, mesager, mulțime, muritor, mut, pion, ploios, rucsac, salcie, sete, Sirop, talentat, țar, ucenic, umflat. (30 words). See www.websters-online-dictionary.org

Puzzle #40: Level 1 - Not So Easy

© Philip M. Parker, INSEAD; www.websters-online-dictionary.org

Across

2 carpenter
4 irresponsible
5 sleepy
6 chaotic
12 homage
15 angular
18 foreman
20 hereditary
21 ludicrous
23 hysterical
25 phosphate
27 adventurous
28 famine, starvation
29 ostensible, seeming
30 ore

Down

1 pilgrimage
3 extinct
7 curly
8 witty
9 earthquake
10 greeting
11 slavery
13 hideous
14 visibility
16 freezer
17 skiing
19 missionary
22 baptism
24 mustard
26 guts

Solutions: aparent, aventuros, botez, Congelator, cutremur, dulgher, ereditar, foamete, fosfat, haotic, hidos, iresponsabil, isteric, maistru, maţe, minereu, misionar, mort, muştar, omagiu, ondulat, pelerinaj, ridicol, salut, Schi, sclavie, somnoros, spiritual, unghiular, vizibilitate. (30 words). See www.websters-online-dictionary.org

Puzzle #41:   Level 1 - A Bit Tough

© Philip M. Parker, INSEAD; www.websters-online-dictionary.org

Across

3 rhetorical
5 aquatic
8 enlightenment
9 lush
12 awfully
13 homeland
15 unavoidable
16 dignified
18 almighty
21 bane, misadventure, misfortune
22 timely
24 quarterly
26 defiance
27 millionaire
28 hybrid

Down

1 sod
2 pamphlet
4 tailor
6 coke
7 psychiatrist
10 roast
11 stately
13 pleading
14 glider
17 inappropriate, unbecoming, undue
18 advantageous
19 prehistoric
20 gloss
23 scar
25 steam, vapour

Solutions: abur, acvatic, atotputernic, avantajos, cicatrice, cocs, croitor, demn, falnic, frige, gazon, hibrid, iluminism, inevitabil, luciu, luxuriant, milionar, nenorocire, nepotrivit, oportun, pamflet, patrie, planor, pledoarie, preistoric, psihiatru, retoric, sfidare, teribil, trimestrial. (30 words). See www.websters-online-dictionary.org

Puzzle #42: Level 1 - A Bit Tough

© Philip M. Parker, INSEAD; www.websters-online-dictionary.org

Across

2 sparkling
4 quay
6 camel
7 unbearable
13 jewel
15 benevolent
17 illegitimate
18 proprietary
21 battalion
23 sensual
24 drown
26 archaic
29 boar
30 viscount

Down

1 dishonest
3 folder
5 carp
8 lottery
9 scarce, sparse
10 searchlight, spotlight
11 liar
12 prophet
14 ounce
16 preacher
19 explosion, outbreak, outburst
20 dice
22 technician
25 athlete
27 bud
28 pious

Solutions: arhaic, atlet, batalion, Bijuterie, binevoitor, boboc, brevetat, cămilă, chei, crap, îneca, insuportabil, izbucnire, loterie, mincinos, necinstit, nelegitim, pios, pliant, predicator, profet, rar, reflector, senzual, spumos, tehnician, uncie, Viconte, vier, Zaruri. (30 words). See www.websters-online-dictionary.org

Puzzle #43:   Level 1 - A Bit Tough

© Philip M. Parker, INSEAD; www.websters-online-dictionary.org

Across

2 phenomenal
5 resumption
7 stocking
10 jade
11 humanitarian
12 sleek
14 pink, rosy
15 clown
19 believer
21 envoy
23 sewing
24 soda
25 claimant
27 cider
28 chronological

Down

1 rash
3 lyrical
4 disapproval
6 ruby
7 clear, limpid, luminous
8 overweight
9 paste
13 pollen
16 walnut
17 devious
18 caller
19 exhaustive
20 indefinite
22 amen
26 cube

Solutions: amin, cidru, ciorap, clar, Clovn, complet, credincios, cronologic, cub, cusut, dezaprobare, fenomenal, jad, lins, liric, nedefinit, nuc, ocolit, pap, polen, pretendent, pripit, reluare, roz, Rubin, sifon, supragreutate, trimis, umanitar, vizitator. (30 words). See www.websters-online-dictionary.org

Puzzle #44: Level 1 - A Bit Tough

© Philip M. Parker, INSEAD; www.websters-online-dictionary.org

Across

1 strife
2 mammal
10 chlorine
12 tyranny
13 hysteria
14 hem
17 humidity
18 dregs, yeast
22 deference
24 grievous
26 glaring
27 arson
28 coy, timid
29 harmonious

Down

1 chronology
3 mechanic
4 hostage
5 overcoat
6 folly, stupidity
7 intruder
8 disarmament
9 lesion
11 folding
15 suffrage
16 terrestrial
19 unreal
20 assassin
21 yoghurt
23 embroidery
25 plum

Solutions: armonios, asasin, broderie, clor, conflict, cronologie, dezarmare, drojdie, dureros, iaurt, incendiere, ireal, isterie, leziune, mamifer, mecanic, nepoftit, orbitor, ostatic, pardesiu, prostie, prună, rabatabil, respect, sfios, terestru, tiranie, Tiv, umiditate, vot. (30 words). See www.websters-online-dictionary.org

Puzzle #45: Level 1 - A Bit Tough

© Philip M. Parker, INSEAD; www.websters-online-dictionary.org

Across

1 motorist
3 snack
4 badger
6 softness
9 nasal
10 cynicism
13 attentive, observant, regardful
17 null
19 spice
20 relay
21 disadvantage, drawback
24 torrent
25 raincoat
26 assortment
27 deadlock

Down

1 topical
2 humility
5 blindness
7 courier
8 dagger
11 plumage
12 souvenir
13 affiliation
14 molten
15 illicit
16 immortal
18 hydraulic
22 fat, fatty
23 spurious
25 anthem

Solutions: actual, afiliere, Asortiment, atent, automobilist, bursuc, cinism, condiment, curier, dezavantaj, fals, gras, gustare, hidraulic, ilicit, imn, impas, impermeabil, moliciune, nazal, nemuritor, nul, orbire, penaj, pumnal, releu, smerenie, Suvenir, topit, torent. (30 words). See www.websters-online-dictionary.org

Puzzle #46: Level 1 - Not Very Tricky

© Philip M. Parker, INSEAD; www.websters-online-dictionary.org

Across

2 mysterious, uncanny
4 bosom
6 oblivion
10 fuselage
12 frightful, horrid
14 corrosion
15 pore
16 quaint
17 fluffy
18 fugitive, runaway
20 lobster
24 livery
25 stiffness
29 sardonic
30 sequel

Down

1 folklore
3 extant
5 phonetic
7 visionary
8 adept
9 stag
11 morphology
13 convict
19 workable
21 rabbi
22 parchment
23 worldly
26 gallop
27 thrush
28 measles

Solutions: batjocoritor, burlac, ciudat, condamnat, coroziune, existent, expert, folclor, fonetic, fugar, fuzelaj, galop, groaznic, Homar, imaginar, livrea, lumesc, misterios, morfologie, pergament, pojar, por, pufos, rabin, realizabil, rigiditate, sturz, suflet, uitare, urmare. (30 words). See www.websters-online-dictionary.org

Puzzle #47: Level 1 - Not Very Tricky

© Philip M. Parker, INSEAD; www.websters-online-dictionary.org

Across

1 fir
3 tapestry
5 sumptuous
8 sender
11 unproductive
12 advantage, vantage
14 usher
15 kernel, pulp
16 bookseller
20 moth
21 canyon
23 smoky
24 paddock
26 salient
27 frosty
28 mimic
29 sob

Down

2 inorganic
4 beehive, hive
6 lantern
7 symposium
9 resilience
10 commercial, mercantile
13 playwright
17 occupant
18 sedate, serene
19 mountainous
22 illustrious
24 poker
25 courageous, spirited

Solutions: afumat, anorganic, avantaj, brad, calm, Canion, comercial, curajos, dramaturg, elasticitate, expeditor, Felinar, geros, ilustru, imitator, librar, miez, molie, muntos, neproductiv, ocupant, padoc, plasator, pocher, proeminent, simpozion, somptuos, stup, suspin, tapiserie. (30 words). See www.websters-online-dictionary.org

Puzzle #48: Level 1 - Not Very Tricky

© Philip M. Parker, INSEAD; www.websters-online-dictionary.org

Across

7 plumber
9 obituary
10 pitiful
11 asparagus
13 allergy
14 snag
16 venom
17 debatable
22 piquant, racy, spicy
24 hypocrisy
25 slang
26 orchid
27 cashier
28 nominee

Down

1 remembrance
2 sodden
3 uproar
4 knack
5 forlorn
6 cyclist
7 immigrant
8 eatable, edible
12 resilient
15 chic
16 ship, steamer
18 falcon
19 boon
20 heresy
21 tremor
23 treatise

Solutions: Alergie, amintire, argou, biciclist, candidat, casier, ciot, comestibil, discutabil, elastic, erezie, favoare, fior, imigrant, instalator, ipocrizie, milos, necopt, necrolog, nenorocit, orhidee, picant, pricepere, şic, şoim, sparanghel, tratat, vacarm, Vapor, venin. (30 words). See www.websters-online-dictionary.org

Puzzle #49:   Level 1 - Not Very Tricky

© Philip M. Parker, INSEAD; www.websters-online-dictionary.org

Across

2 nightingale
5 drugstore, pharmacy
8 humanism
10 iceberg
13 poppy
14 tulip
17 equator
19 rhinoceros
24 spinach
26 subway
27 lapel
28 pheasant
29 thermometer

Down

1 sparrow
3 radish
4 hammock
6 raven
7 flea
9 artichoke
11 boulevard, avenue
12 isotope
15 oyster
16 zipper
18 propeller
20 ox
21 leek
22 melon
23 shutter
24 sonnet
25 beaver

Solutions: Aisberg, anghinare, bou, bulevard, castor, corb, ecuator, Elice, Farmacie, Fazan, fermoar, hamac, izotop, Lalea, mac, metrou, oblon, Pepene, praz, privighetoare, purice, rever, Ridiche, rinocer, sonet, spanac, stridie, termometru, umanism, vrabie. (30 words). See www.websters-online-dictionary.org

Puzzle #50:   Level 1 - Not Very Tricky

© Philip M. Parker, INSEAD; www.websters-online-dictionary.org

Across

4 starling
5 aircraft, airplane, aeroplane
7 harbor
8 ostrich
9 flax
11 oboe
13 accordion
14 ladle
20 etymology
22 poplar
23 grapefruit
25 staid, demure, earnest
26 navel
27 shipwreck
28 marten

Down

1 color
2 kangaroo
3 pumpkin
6 polecat
8 shrew, virago
10 encyclopedia
12 starch
15 liqueur
16 skier
17 atheism
18 suspenders
19 hippopotamus
21 tripod
24 louse
25 sled, sleigh, toboggan

Solutions: acordeon, amidon, ateism, avion, bretele, buric, Cangur, Culoare, dihor, Dovleac, Enciclopedie, etimologie, graur, Grepfrut, Hipopotam, in, jder, lichior, Naufragiu, oboi, păduche, plop, polonic, Port, Sanie, schior, scorpie, serios, struț, Trepied. (30 words). See www.websters-online-dictionary.org

Puzzle #51:   Level 1 - A Bit Tricky

© Philip M. Parker, INSEAD; www.websters-online-dictionary.org

Across

4 base, sordid
7 casino
9 harmless, innocuous
10 spherical
11 selfishness
13 humanist
16 allegory
18 faucet
21 clover
22 deacon
25 opaque
26 mammoth
27 phoneme
28 unfriendly

Down

1 taboo
2 pedestal
3 projector
5 glassy
6 sew
8 elm
12 emerald
14 espionage
15 appetizer
16 anthology
17 graphite
19 copious
20 fateful
22 stench, stink
23 beefsteak, steak
24 juicy

Solutions: abundent, alegorie, antologie, Aperitiv, biftec, Cazinou, coase, diacon, duhoare, egoism, fatal, fonem, grafit, inofensiv, josnic, mamut, neprietenos, opac, piedestal, proiector, Robinet, sferic, smarald, spionaj, sticlos, tabu, trifoi, ulm, umanist, zemos. (30 words). See www.websters-online-dictionary.org

Puzzle #52: Level 1 - A Bit Tricky

Across

1 inexorable
5 sundry
8 quartz
12 robber
15 orphanage
17 starboard
18 immoral
19 discount, rebate
22 pessimism
23 wick
25 squalor
26 sanitary
27 feverish
28 weighty

Down

2 accomplice
3 beige
4 noxious
5 disinterested
6 vineyard
7 howl
9 deafness
10 envious, jealous
11 diver
13 cylindrical
14 labyrinth
16 pilgrim
17 theorist
20 wren
21 mysticism
24 honest, righteous

Solutions: bej, cilindric, cinstit, complice, cuarţ, dezinteresat, divers, febril, Fitil, igienic, imoral, implacabil, important, invidios, jefuitor, labirint, misticism, mizerie, nociv, orfelinat, pelerin, pesimism, Pitulice, rabat, scafandru, surzenie, teoretician, tribord, urlet, vie. (30 words). See www.websters-online-dictionary.org

Puzzle #53: Level 1 - A Bit Tricky

© Philip M. Parker, INSEAD; www.websters-online-dictionary.org

Across

8 passivity
10 sanitation
14 axle
15 thyme
16 phosphorus
21 mime
22 unbalanced
26 unprofitable
28 lowly
29 orphan
30 plywood

Down

1 soot
2 ruddy
3 trajectory
4 shroud
5 bankrupt, insolvent
6 trump
7 roe, spawn
9 waltz
11 gunner
12 psychiatry
13 veneer
17 lobe
18 chimpanzee
19 gaiety, mirth
20 oppressor, tyrant
23 cedar
24 annals
25 gable
27 mascara

Solutions: anale, atu, cedru, cimbru, cimpanzeu, dezechilibrat, falit, fosfor, fronton, funingine, furnir, giulgiu, Icre, lob, mim, modest, nerentabil, orfan, osie, pasivitate, placaj, psihiatrie, rimel, rumen, salubritate, tiran, traiectorie, tunar, vals, veselie. (30 words). See www.websters-online-dictionary.org

Puzzle #54: Level 1 - A Bit Tricky

Across

3 mauve
6 medley
7 methodical
10 immorality
13 penniless
16 forked
17 assignee
19 dowry
21 submissive
22 preposterous
23 encore
24 reindeer
25 constabulary
26 teller
27 eel
28 irrevocable

Down

1 seduction
2 thistle
3 wistful
4 bridegroom
5 watchman
8 orgy
9 slime
11 ebony
12 equatorial
14 homicide
15 averse
18 allusion
20 desertion
21 thorny

Solutions: abanos, absurd, aluzie, amestec, bifurcat, bis, cesionar, ciulin, dezertare, ecuatorial, farmec, imoralitate, irevocabil, jandarmerie, lefter, melancolic, metodic, mire, mov, noroi, omucidere, orgie, paznic, potrivnic, povestitor, ren, spinos, supus, țipar, zestre. (30 words). See www.websters-online-dictionary.org

Puzzle #55: Level 1 - A Bit Tricky

© Philip M. Parker, INSEAD; www.websters-online-dictionary.org

Across

2 supposition
5 gait
6 nakedness
7 snout
10 harpsichord
12 typist
13 venomous
16 rationalism
19 ether
22 blizzard
23 bearable
26 hypocrite
28 adventurer
29 conqueror

Down

1 archipelago
3 avoidable
4 furrow, line
8 opportunist
9 unfaithful
11 wad
14 surrealism
15 nobleman
17 monsoon
18 disorderly
20 suffix
21 mystic
22 reverie
24 crane, winch
25 nudge
27 barter

Solutions: arhipelag, aventurier, bot, clavecin, cuceritor, dactilograf, dezordonat, eter, evitabil, ghiont, goliciune, infidel, ipocrit, macara, mers, mistic, muson, nobil, oportunist, presupunere, raţionalism, rid, sufix, suportabil, suprarealism, tampon, troc, veninos, visare, viscol. (30 words). See www.websters-online-dictionary.org

Puzzle #56: Level 1 - Tricky

Across

2 brevity
3 cypress
5 slipper
8 disorderly, riotous
10 pathos
12 elliptical
14 billion, trillion
15 nitric
17 thermostat
19 plaid
22 millet
23 cowardice
26 irregularity
27 gaseous
28 heroism

Down

1 synonym
4 foray
6 motley, promiscuous
7 sucker
9 quits
11 hospitable
13 movable
16 shoemaker
18 chastity
19 passive, quiescent
20 purposely
21 lethargy
22 fastidious
24 pang, twinge
25 hurricane, tornado

Solutions: amestecat, azotic, Bilion, castitate, Chiparos, chit, cizmar, concizie, dinadins, eliptic, eroism, gazos, incursiune, junghi, laşitate, letargie, mei, mobil, mofturos, neregularitate, ospitalier, papuc, pasiv, patos, Pled, sinonim, sugar, termostat, turbulent, uragan. (30 words). See www.websters-online-dictionary.org

Puzzle #57: Level 1 - Tricky

© Philip M. Parker, INSEAD; www.websters-online-dictionary.org

Across

1 quizzical
7 amphitheatre
8 outcast
10 ethereal
11 nickel
12 sapphire
13 uninhabited
14 trowel
17 greenish
18 apparition
20 affable, amiable, obliging
21 artful, wily
22 ponderous
24 stalwart
25 harlequin
26 perfunctory

Down

2 chaste
3 pallor
4 heredity
5 pattern, sitter
6 leech
8 unremitting
9 narration
14 prodigy
15 rheumatism
16 derogatory
19 jasmine
21 vassal
23 indistinct
24 sorrel

Solutions: amabil, amfiteatru, arlechin, cast, ereditate, eteric, greoi, iasomie, ironic, lipitoare, minune, mistrie, Model, neclar, nelocuit, nichel, paloare, peiorativ, perseverent, proscris, relatare, reumatism, robust, Roib, safir, superficial, vasal, vedenie, verzui, viclean. (30 words). See www.websters-online-dictionary.org

Puzzle #58: Level 1 - Tricky

© Philip M. Parker, INSEAD; www.websters-online-dictionary.org

Across

1 courtier
3 fluff
6 inhabitant
7 pert, saucy
9 fiend
11 itinerant
13 basalt
14 chromium
17 asperity, roughness
22 couplet
23 flabby
24 irreducible
25 kaleidoscope
26 ointment
27 scholastic
28 spaniel

Down

2 ammonium
3 pus
4 celluloid
5 coachman
8 innkeeper
10 peculiarity
12 nothingness
15 opportunism
16 chandelier
17 airman
18 euphemism
19 counterpoint
20 unobserved
21 cloudless, serene

Solutions: alifie, ambulant, amoniu, asprime, aviator, bazalt, caleidoscop, candelabru, celuloid, contrapunct, crom, cuplet, curtean, diavol, eufemism, flasc, hangiu, ireductibil, locuitor, neobservat, nimicnicie, obraznic, oportunism, particularitate, prepelicar, puf, puroi, scolastic, senin, vizitiu. (30 words). See www.websters-online-dictionary.org

Puzzle #59: Level 1 - Tricky

Across

1 scooter
3 pulley
4 fickle, whimsical
7 rabies
9 dynamo
11 prodigal, spender
17 ephemeral
18 deformity
20 amphibious
23 slave, thrall
25 horned
26 tonnage
27 tributary
29 fission

Down

2 stilts
5 onlooker
6 balm
8 bureaucrat
10 downcast
12 sprinkler
13 anchoret, hermit, recluse
14 boatman
15 confessor
16 odyssey
17 ecstasy, rapture
19 sheepish, shy
21 asphalt
22 poodle
24 greedy, voracious
28 spindle

Solutions: afluent, amfibiu, asfalt, balsam, barcagiu, birocrat, capricios, catalige, cornut, deprimat, diformitate, dinam, duhovnic, efemer, extaz, fisiune, fus, lacom, odisee, pudel, pustnic, risipitor, sclav, scripete, scuter, spectator, stropitoare, timid, tonaj, turbare. (30 words). See www.websters-online-dictionary.org

Puzzle #60:   Level 1 - Tricky

© Philip M. Parker, INSEAD; www.websters-online-dictionary.org

Across

2 demonstrator
7 vagrant
10 sewerage
12 auspicious, propitious
16 equestrian
17 morose, surly
18 manger
20 bricklayer
21 greengrocer
22 locket
26 pollination
27 hilarity
28 iodine
29 woodpecker
30 python

Down

1 tadpole
3 fireman, stoker
4 preternatural,
   unearthly
5 corkscrew
6 rabid
8 crusader
9 whey
11 thrifty
13 zeppelin
14 mildew
15 behavior
19 syllabic
23 larynx
24 thermos
25 tailoring

Solutions: canalizare, ciocănitoare, croitorie, cruciat, econom, ecvestru, favorabil, fochist, iesle, ilaritate, iod, laringe, manifestant, medalion, mormoloc, mucegai, piton, polenizare, purtare, silabic, supranatural, termos, tirbuşon, turbat, ursuz, vagabond, zarzavagiu, Zepelin, zer, zidar. (30 words). See www.websters-online-dictionary.org

Puzzle #61:   Level 1 - Pretty Tricky

© Philip M. Parker, INSEAD; www.websters-online-dictionary.org

Across

3 scurrilous
6 fingernail, nail
8 cynic
9 jaundice
10 ochre
11 purr
12 kayak
15 cyclone
16 belligerent
18 breakwater
22 penknife
23 trachea
24 climber, mountaineer
25 storehouse
26 alligator
28 woodcock
29 abstruse, furtive, recondite
30 prolongation

Down

1 renown
2 smallness
4 protractor
5 throaty
7 inaccuracy
13 tyrannical
14 insincere
17 leper
19 portly
20 fatality
21 servitude
27 laziness, sloth

Solutions: Aligator, Alpinist, ascuns, beligerant, briceag, Caiac, calamitate, ciclon, cinic, corpolent, depozit, dig, gutural, icter, inexactitate, injurios, lene, lepros, micime, nesincer, ocru, prelungire, raportor, renume, robie, Sitar, tiranic, tors, trahee, unghie. (30 words). See www.websters-online-dictionary.org

Puzzle #62:   Level 1 - Pretty Tricky

© Philip M. Parker, INSEAD; www.websters-online-dictionary.org

Across

2 cannibal
6 pyre
7 torrid
8 homesickness
11 lecherous, lewd
13 jocular
16 tobacconist
19 minuet
21 papyrus
23 collectivity
27 discoverer
28 mush
29 minstrel
30 shortness

Down

1 pylon
3 alum
4 purveyor
5 settler
9 satchel
10 liveliness
12 steadfast
14 annunciation
15 entire, unmitigated
17 usurper
18 disinfectant
20 philology
22 obsequious, servile
24 superman
25 dwarf, manikin, midget
26 volleyball

Solutions: alaun, canibal, colectivitate, colonist, comic, descoperitor, dezinfectant, filologie, furnizor, ghiozdan, libidinos, menestrel, menuet, nostalgie, papirus, pilon, pitic, rug, scurtime, slugarnic, stabil, supraom, terci, torid, total, tutungiu, uzurpator, vestire, vioiciune, Volei. (30 words). See www.websters-online-dictionary.org

Puzzle #63: Level 1 - Pretty Tricky

© Philip M. Parker, INSEAD; www.websters-online-dictionary.org

Across

2 malleable, tractable
5 wanderer
8 adornment
10 tannin
14 lithography
16 bison
17 upstart
18 sightless
26 confection
27 roundness
28 pessimist
29 stormy, tempestuous

Down

1 freemasonry
3 abscess
4 jester, zany
6 quince
7 inedible
8 abhorrence
9 bivouac
11 midshipman
12 smuggler
13 udder
15 turnip
19 asunder
20 mortification
21 brisk, mercurial, snappy
22 bookish
23 zealot
24 typhoon
25 ferrous

Solutions: abces, aspirant, bivuac, bizon, bufon, contrabandist, dulciuri, fanatic, feros, francmasonerie, furtunos, Gutuie, hoinar, litografie, livresc, maleabil, nap, necomestibil, orb, ornament, oroare, parvenit, pesimist, rotunjime, separat, taifun, tanin, uger, umilire, vioi. (30 words). See www.websters-online-dictionary.org

Puzzle #64:   Level 1 - Pretty Tricky

© Philip M. Parker, INSEAD; www.websters-online-dictionary.org

Across

5 collectivization
6 skunk
9 wart
12 effusion
13 haughty, overbearing
15 nonentity
16 adieu
17 bartender
20 engraver
26 dustman
27 deserter
28 skilful, versed
29 hypodermic
30 projectile

Down

1 acme, apogee, summit
2 cyst
3 rumpus
4 vagrancy
7 tiresome, wearisome
8 satyr
10 glazier
11 aphorism
14 turbid
18 troubadour
19 excerpt
21 technologist
22 gnarled, knotty
23 stationer
24 drinkable
25 suet, tallow

Solutions: adio, aforism, arogant, Barman, chist, colectivizare, culme, dezertor, efuziune, fragment, geamgiu, gravor, gunoier, neg, noduros, nulitate, obositor, papetar, potabil, priceput, proiectil, satir, scandal, sconcs, seu, subcutanat, tehnolog, trubadur, tulbure, vagabondaj. (30 words). See www.websters-online-dictionary.org

Puzzle #65: Level 1 - Pretty Tricky

Across

1 mannerism
4 hornet
5 inequity
7 ticklish
8 pomegranate
10 speedometer
11 janitor
12 manikin, mannequin
14 cur
15 welder
16 northerner
20 skiff
22 seemly
24 italic
26 equilateral
27 titter
28 sad, sorrowful, woeful

Down

2 superhuman
3 inattentive
5 untiring
6 diphthong
9 fop
13 tassel
15 sentient
17 elocution
18 honeyed, unctuous
19 anthracite
21 guffaw
23 hurrah
25 isthmus

Solutions: antracit, chicot, ciucure, cursiv, decent, dificil, diftong, echilateral, filfizon, hohot, istm, manechin, manierism, mieros, neatent, nedreptate, neobosit, nordic, oratorie, portar, potaie, rodie, schif, sensibil, Sudor, supraomenesc, trist, ura, viespe, vitezometru. (30 words). See www.websters-online-dictionary.org

Puzzle #66: Level 1 - A Bit Advanced

© Philip M. Parker, INSEAD; www.websters-online-dictionary.org

Across

3 wheelwright
5 baccy
7 camphor
8 polygamy
10 wrecker
11 ruffian
16 zephyr
17 cock, rooster
19 piteous, pitiable
24 dahlia
25 tomcat
27 swordsman
28 juggler
29 aesthete
30 bawl

Down

1 physiognomy
2 bagpipe
4 tympanum
6 confectioner
9 xylophone
12 vapid
13 bloodhound
14 dysentery
15 rickets
18 overwrought
20 slanderous
21 amiability
22 boomerang
23 lentil
26 peppery

Solutions: amabilitate, bandit, bumerang, calomnios, camfor, cimpoi, cocoş, cofetar, copoi, dalie, diversionist, dizenterie, estet, fizionomie, insipid, jalnic, jongler, linte, motan, piperat, poligamie, rahitism, rotar, spadasin, surescitat, tabac, timpan, xilofon, zbieret, zefir. (30 words). See www.websters-online-dictionary.org

Puzzle #67: Level 1 - A Bit Advanced

© Philip M. Parker, INSEAD; www.websters-online-dictionary.org

Across

5 humorist
8 lackey
10 warble
12 mumps
13 blackleg, swindler
15 alembic
16 annular
18 gimlet
22 trousseau
23 neuralgia
24 sweetish
26 gymnast
27 truant
28 anthrax
29 syllogism

Down

1 jewelry
2 scurvy
3 sympathizer
4 pharynx
6 mourner
7 peony
9 docker, stevedore
11 polyglot
14 muffler
15 ammeter
17 pardonable
19 haberdashery
20 assiduity
21 obsequies
25 billow

Solutions: alambic, ampermetru, asiduitate, Bijuterii, bocitoare, bujor, chiulangiu, ciripit, dalac, docher, dulceag, escroc, faringe, fular, funeralii, gimnast, inelar, lacheu, mercerie, nevralgie, oreion, poliglot, scorbut, scuzabil, sfredel, silogism, simpatizant, talaz, trusou, umorist. (30 words). See www.websters-online-dictionary.org

Puzzle #68:   Level 1 - A Bit Advanced

© Philip M. Parker, INSEAD; www.websters-online-dictionary.org

Across

3 embezzlement, peculation
5 gusset
6 freckle
8 vermicelli
12 philately
13 quadruped
14 freemason
15 hydrate
16 exigent
17 brassiere
21 wordiness
23 kerchief, neckerchief
25 gluey
26 mesmerism
29 archaism
30 skittle

Down

1 tripper
2 acclimation
4 factitious
7 illiterate, unlettered
9 quadrille
10 unpractical
11 underfed
18 tare
19 impolite, uncivil
20 penmanship
22 homonym
24 ingot
27 billion, milliard
28 wisecrack

Solutions: aclimatizare, analfabet, arhaism, artificial, banc, batic, cadril, caligrafie, clin, dara, delapidare, excursionist, fidea, filatelie, francmason, hidrat, hipnotism, lingou, lipicios, Miliard, nepoliticos, nepractic, omonim, patruped, pistrui, popic, prolixitate, subnutrit, Sutien, urgent. (30 words). See www.websters-online-dictionary.org

Puzzle #69: Level 1 - A Bit Advanced

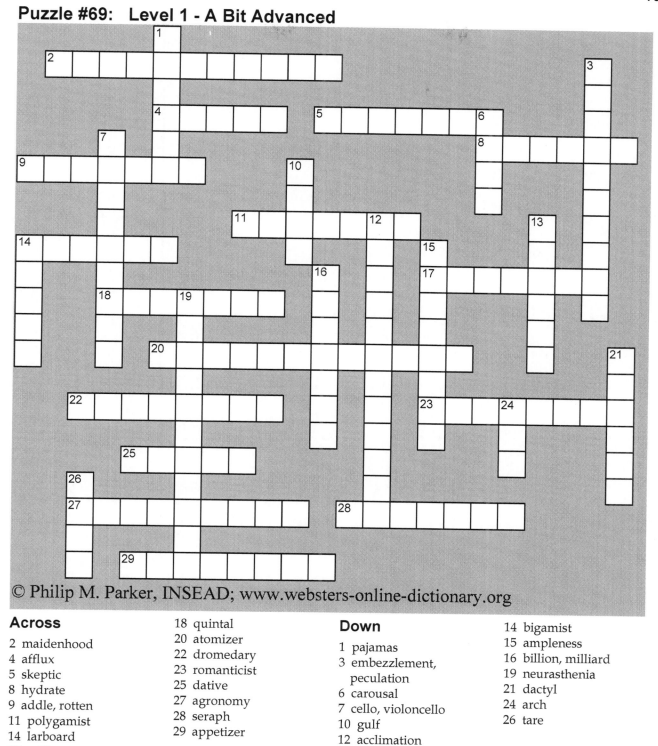

© Philip M. Parker, INSEAD; www.websters-online-dictionary.org

Across

2 maidenhood
4 afflux
5 skeptic
8 hydrate
9 addle, rotten
11 polygamist
14 larboard
17 millenary
18 quintal
20 atomizer
22 dromedary
23 romanticist
25 dative
27 agronomy
28 seraph
29 appetizer

Down

1 pajamas
3 embezzlement,
   peculation
6 carousal
7 cello, violoncello
10 gulf
12 acclimation
13 pennon
14 bigamist
15 ampleness
16 billion, milliard
19 neurasthenia
21 dactyl
24 arch
26 tare

Solutions: aclimatizare, aflux, agronomie, amploare, Aperitiv, Arc, babord, bigam, chef, chintal, dactil, dara, dativ, delapidare, dromader, fanion, golf, hidrat, milenar, Miliard, neurastenie, pijama, poligam, pulverizator, romantic, sceptic, serafim, stricat, violoncel, virginitate. (30 words). See www.websters-online-dictionary.org

Puzzle #70:   Level 1 - Just for Fun

© Philip M. Parker, INSEAD; www.websters-online-dictionary.org

Across

3 atomizer
4 pajamas
9 philately
10 maidenhood
14 hexameter
18 tripper
19 archaism
20 quintal
23 vermicelli
24 mesmerism
26 quadruped
27 exigent
28 parasite, sponger
29 somnambulist
30 afflux

Down

1 breviary
2 penmanship
5 millenary
6 pennon
7 wordiness
8 wisecrack
11 factitious
12 larboard
13 kerchief, neckerchief
15 antonym
16 sentimentalist
17 mulatto
21 ingot
22 carousal
25 quadrille

Solutions: aflux, antonim, arhaism, artificial, babord, banc, batic, breviar, cadril, caligrafie, chef, chintal, excursionist, fanion, fidea, filatelie, hexametru, hipnotism, lingou, milenar, mulatru, parazit, patruped, pijama, prolixitate, pulverizator, sentimental, somnambul, urgent, virginitate. (30 words). See www.websters-online-dictionary.org

Puzzle #71: Level 1 - Just for Fun

© Philip M. Parker, INSEAD; www.websters-online-dictionary.org

Across

3 gimlet
4 homonym
5 sweetish
9 skittle
10 suzerain
13 gluey
15 blackleg, swindler
20 decease
22 onomatopoeia
23 jewelry
24 assiduity
25 precocity
27 beatitude
28 faucet
29 freemason

Down

1 petunia
2 beefsteak, steak
6 vaporous
7 profiteer
8 impolite, uncivil
10 underfed
11 alembic
12 infamy
14 preponderant
16 freckle
17 exportation
18 illiterate, unlettered
19 unpractical
21 brassiere
26 gusset

Solutions: alambic, analfabet, asiduitate, beatitudine, biftec, Bijuterii, clin, deces, dulceag, escroc, exportare, francmason, infamie, lipicios, nepoliticos, nepractic, omonim, onomatopee, petunie, pistrui, popic, precocitate, preponderent, profitor, Robinet, sfredel, subnutrit, Sutien, suzeran, vaporos. (30 words). See www.websters-online-dictionary.org

Puzzle #72:   Level 1 - Just for Fun

© Philip M. Parker, INSEAD; www.websters-online-dictionary.org

Across

1 benighted, ignoramus
5 purgative
7 mourner
10 demagogy
12 lackey
13 polyglot
15 beefsteak, steak
18 muffler
19 warble
20 monorail
21 avidity
25 cordiality
26 obsequies
27 sympathizer
28 gymnast
29 truant

Down

2 billow
3 bigamy
4 grammarian
6 humorist
8 insensibility
9 lexicography
10 anthrax
11 syllogism
14 indisposed
16 parallelogram
17 cadaverous
22 prefab
23 genitive
24 pardonable

Solutions: aviditate, biftec, bigamie, bocitoare, cadaveric, chiulangiu, ciripit, cordialitate, dalac, demagogie, fular, funeralii, genitiv, gimnast, gramatician, ignorant, indispus, insensibilitate, lacheu, lexicografie, Monorai, paralelogram, poliglot, prefabricat, purgativ, scuzabil, silogism, simpatizant, talaz, umorist. (30 words). See www.websters-online-dictionary.org

Puzzle #73:   Level 1 - Just for Fun

© Philip M. Parker, INSEAD; www.websters-online-dictionary.org

Across

2 haberdashery
5 antipathetic
8 ruffian
10 scurvy
11 mumps
16 paroxysm
17 participle
21 strontium
22 neuralgia
23 zephyr
25 slanderous
26 perfidious
28 docker, stevedore
29 vigour, vim
30 trousseau

Down

1 pharynx
3 aesthete
4 vermouth
6 annular
7 peony
9 libertine
12 iridium
13 cock, rooster
14 bagpipe
15 tympanum
18 ammeter
19 stenographer
20 demagogue
24 festoon
27 polecat

Solutions: ampermetru, antipatic, bandit, bujor, calomnios, cimpoi, cocoş, demagog, dihor, docher, estet, faringe, feston, inelar, iridiu, libertin, mercerie, nevralgie, oreion, paroxism, participiu, perfid, scorbut, stenograf, stronţiu, timpan, trusou, vermut, vigoare, zefir. (30 words). See www.websters-online-dictionary.org

Puzzle #74: Level 1 - Just for Fun

© Philip M. Parker, INSEAD; www.websters-online-dictionary.org

Across

1 obscene, ribald, smutty
3 baccy
5 asperity
7 carmine
8 bawl
11 physiognomy
13 periscope
16 conjugation
17 telegraphy
20 trigonometry
23 wrecker
25 bloodhound
26 tomcat
27 confectioner
28 polygamy
29 dahlia

Down

2 swordsman
4 amiability
6 wheelwright
9 boomerang
10 lentil
12 artichoke
14 camphor
15 peppery
16 cataclysm
18 rickets
19 xylophone
21 juggler
22 sled, sleigh, toboggan
24 vapid

Solutions: amabilitate, anghinare, asperitate, bumerang, camfor, carmin, cataclism, cofetar, conjugare, copoi, dalie, diversionist, fizionomie, insipid, jongler, linte, motan, obscen, periscop, piperat, poligamie, rahitism, rotar, sanie, spadasin, tabac, telegrafie, trigonometrie, xilofon, zbieret. (30 words). See www.websters-online-dictionary.org

Puzzle #75: Level 1 - Just for Fun

© Philip M. Parker, INSEAD; www.websters-online-dictionary.org

Across

1 ventricle
5 honeyed, unctuous
7 pomegranate
9 manikin, mannequin
10 intransitive
13 skiff
16 overwrought
21 seemly
22 caprice, fad, whim
24 piteous, pitiable
25 guffaw
27 elocution
28 northerner
29 retroactive
30 dysentery

Down

2 convexity
3 cur
4 ticklish
6 spore
8 sled, sleigh, toboggan
11 untiring
12 speedometer
14 scruple
15 tassel
17 titter
18 tricolour
19 indissoluble
20 fop
23 anarchism
26 janitor

Solutions: anarhism, capriciu, chicot, ciucure, convexitate, decent, dificil, dizenterie, filfizon, hohot, indisolubil, intranzitiv, jalnic, manechin, mieros, neobosit, nordic, oratorie, portar, potaie, retroactiv, rodie, Sanie, schif, scrupul, spor, surescitat, tricolor, ventricul, vitezometru. (30 words). See www.websters-online-dictionary.org

Puzzle #76: Level 1 - Just for Fun

© Philip M. Parker, INSEAD; www.websters-online-dictionary.org

Across

2 sentient
4 debility
6 determinative
9 harpoon
12 silo
14 inattentive
16 italic
19 hurrah
21 stiletto
24 megaphone
25 superhuman
26 neglectful, remiss, slipshod
28 mannerism
29 anthracite

Down

1 welder
3 banality, triviality
5 antimony
7 microbe
8 sad, sorrowful, woeful
10 hornet
11 hippopotamus
13 pariah
14 inequity
15 laureate
17 interrogative
18 equilateral
20 diphthong
22 credulous
23 semicircle
27 isthmus

Solutions: antimoniu, antracit, banalitate, credul, cursiv, debilitate, determinant, diftong, echilateral, harpon, Hipopotam, interogativ, istm, laureat, manierism, Megafon, microb, neatent, nedreptate, neglijent, paria, semicerc, sensibil, siloz, stilet, Sudor, supraomenesc, trist, ura, viespe. (30 words). See www.websters-online-dictionary.org

Puzzle #77: Level 1 - Just for Fun

© Philip M. Parker, INSEAD; www.websters-online-dictionary.org

Across

1 excerpt
5 stationer
7 nonentity
10 tiresome, wearisome
11 convulsion
13 voltmeter
16 dustman
18 incorruptible
25 collectivization
26 sardine
27 technologist
28 trapeze
29 deserter
30 glazier

Down

2 effusion
3 drinkable
4 acme, apogee, summit
6 adieu
8 lascivious
9 ostracism
12 suet, tallow
14 projectile
15 paralytic
17 wart
19 skunk
20 rumpus
21 vagrancy
22 pedantry
23 turbid
24 semester

Solutions: adio, colectivizare, convulsie, culme, dezertor, efuziune, fragment, geamgiu, gunoier, incoruptibil, lasciv, neg, nulitate, obositor, ostracizare, papetar, paralitic, pedanterie, potabil, proiectil, sardea, scandal, sconcs, semestru, seu, tehnolog, trapez, tulbure, vagabondaj, voltmetru. (30 words). See www.websters-online-dictionary.org

Puzzle #78:   Level 1 - Just for Fun

Across

1 freemasonry
6 engraver
7 macaroni
9 bartender
12 satyr
13 cyst
14 menagerie
15 pessimist
17 turnip
21 voluble
23 neurology
24 abacus
25 notary
26 quince
28 abscess
29 skilful, versed

Down

2 haughty, overbearing
3 gnarled, knotty
4 brisk, mercurial, snappy
5 monotheism
8 aphorism
9 suspenders
10 lithography
11 roundness
16 hypodermic
18 mortification
19 trill
20 troubadour
22 sightless
27 udder

Solutions: abac, abces, aforism, arogant, Barman, bretele, chist, francmasonerie, gravor, Gutuie, litografie, macaroane, menajerie, monoteism, nap, neurologie, noduros, notar, orb, pesimist, priceput, rotunjime, satir, subcutanat, tril, trubadur, uger, umilire, vioi, volubil. (30 words). See www.websters-online-dictionary.org

Puzzle #79:   Level 1 - Just for Fun

© Philip M. Parker, INSEAD; www.websters-online-dictionary.org

Across

2 smuggler
5 etymology
8 combustible
9 plagiarism
15 bivouac
16 inedible
17 abhorrence
20 louse
21 orifice
22 monocle
24 albatross
26 sacrilege
28 asunder
29 melodious, tuneful
30 ferrous

Down

1 ductile
3 confection
4 stormy, tempestuous
6 tannin
7 midshipman
10 amethyst
11 zealot
12 timidity
13 malleable, tractable
14 rapacious
18 sedative
19 adornment
23 bookish
25 bison
27 colossus

Solutions: albatros, ametist, aspirant, bivuac, bizon, colos, combustibil, contrabandist, ductil, dulciuri, etimologie, fanatic, feros, furtunos, livresc, maleabil, melodios, monoclu, necomestibil, orificiu, ornament, oroare, păduche, plagiat, rapace, sacrilegiu, sedativ, separat, tanin, timiditate. (30 words). See www.websters-online-dictionary.org

Puzzle #80: Level 1 - Just for Fun

© Philip M. Parker, INSEAD; www.websters-online-dictionary.org

Across

1 transitive
6 impure
7 upstart
10 steadfast
12 ovary
13 philology
16 basement, subsoil
17 jester, zany
18 monolith
21 apogee
23 superlative
25 alchemist
26 recitation
27 torrid
28 cannibal

Down

2 isosceles
3 alum
4 starling
5 biplane
6 inflammable
8 liveliness
9 sonorous
11 typhoon
14 plebiscite
15 wanderer
16 superman
19 interstate
20 semaphore
22 optimistic, sanguine
24 annunciation

Solutions: alaun, alchimist, apogeu, biplan, bufon, canibal, filologie, graur, hoinar, impur, inflamabil, interstatal, isoscel, monolit, optimist, ovar, parvenit, plebiscit, recitare, semafor, sonor, stabil, subsol, superlativ, supraom, taifun, torid, tranzitiv, vestire, vioiciune. (30 words). See www.websters-online-dictionary.org

Puzzle #81: Level 1 - Just for Fun

© Philip M. Parker, INSEAD; www.websters-online-dictionary.org

Across

1 zoologist
3 excess, surfeit
9 minuet
10 telepathy
12 papyrus
14 hammock
19 metallurgy
22 elegy
23 ladle
24 dwarf, manikin, midget
26 pyre
28 irascible
29 lignite
30 mineralogy

Down

2 tulip
4 collectivity
5 strategist
6 sterility
7 tobacconist
8 purveyor
11 homesickness
13 planter
15 usurper
16 subterfuge
17 disinfectant
18 centigrade
20 idolatry
21 zipper
25 epilogue
27 pylon

Solutions: centigrad, colectivitate, dezinfectant, elegie, epilog, exces, fermoar, furnizor, hamac, idolatrie, irascibil, Lalea, lignit, menuet, metalurgie, mineralogie, nostalgie, papirus, pilon, pitic, plantator, polonic, rug, sterilitate, strateg, subterfugiu, telepatie, tutungiu, uzurpator, zoolog. (30 words). See www.websters-online-dictionary.org

Puzzle #82:   Level 1 - Just for Fun

© Philip M. Parker, INSEAD; www.websters-online-dictionary.org

Across

2 settler
5 alligator
7 paternity
10 invader
11 mush
12 satchel
13 trombone
14 lecherous, lewd
17 obsequious, servile
19 storehouse
20 sanatorium
24 throaty
26 inalienable
27 shortness
29 sectarianism
30 smallness

Down

1 jocular
3 impressionism
4 kayak
6 lucidity
8 emissary
9 discoverer
15 monstrosity
16 fillip, stimulant
18 repulsion
21 scurrilous
22 minstrel
23 volleyball
25 studious
28 entire, unmitigated

Solutions: Aligator, Caiac, colonist, comic, depozit, descoperitor, emisar, ghiozdan, gutural, impresionism, inalienabil, injurios, invadator, libidinos, lucidulate, menestrel, micime, monstruozitate, paternitate, repulsie, sanatoriu, scurtime, sectarism, slugarnic, stimulent, studios, terci, total, trombon, Volei. (30 words). See www.websters-online-dictionary.org

Puzzle #83:   Level 1 - Just for Fun

© Philip M. Parker, INSEAD; www.websters-online-dictionary.org

Across

6 fatality
8 monologue, soliloquy
9 saxophone
10 shrew, virago
12 trachea
13 ochre
14 jaundice

16 abstruse, furtive, recondite
18 cyclone
25 virility
26 penknife
28 meteorite
29 microbiology
30 perforation

Down

1 protractor
2 cynic
3 belligerent
4 breakwater
5 inoculation
7 laziness, sloth
11 depravity
15 shipwreck

17 portly
19 insincere
20 perversity
21 fingernail, nail
22 prolongation
23 servitude
24 stethoscope
27 purr

Solutions: ascuns, beligerant, briceag, calamitate, ciclon, cinic, corpolent, depravare, dig, icter, inoculare, lene, meteorit, microbiologie, monolog, Naufragiu, nesincer, ocru, perforare, perversitate, prelungire, raportor, robie, saxofon, scorpie, stetoscop, tors, trahee, unghie, virilitate. (30 words). See www.websters-online-dictionary.org

Puzzle #84:   Level 1 - Just for Fun

© Philip M. Parker, INSEAD; www.websters-online-dictionary.org

Across

1 navigable
5 skier
7 manger
10 inaccuracy
12 marten
13 bricklayer
15 woodcock
16 pumpkin
18 shrew, virago
23 iodine
26 climber, mountaineer
27 lugubrious
28 tadpole
29 recitative

Down

2 lamentable
3 divisible
4 renown
5 preternatural, unearthly
6 hilarity
8 pollination
9 locket
11 tyrannical
14 demonstrative
17 adorable
19 harbor
20 syllabic
21 fireman, stoker
22 baritone
24 leper
25 aircraft, airplane, aeroplane

Solutions: adorabil, Alpinist, avion, bariton, demonstrativ, divizibil, Dovleac, Fochist, iesle, ilaritate, inexactitate, iod, jder, lamentabil, lepros, lugubru, medalion, mormoloc, navigabil, polenizare, Port, recitativ, renume, schior, scorpie, silabic, Sitar, supranatural, tiranic, zidar. (30 words). See www.websters-online-dictionary.org

Puzzle #85:   Level 1 - Just for Fun

© Philip M. Parker, INSEAD; www.websters-online-dictionary.org

Across

2 python
4 vagrant
6 zeppelin
8 obtuse
11 larynx
13 equestrian
14 woodpecker
15 aircraft, airplane, aeroplane
17 mildew
21 rabid
23 morose, surly
24 expressionism
26 epithet
27 impresario
28 behavior
29 auspicious, propitious
30 tailoring

Down

1 demonstrator
3 incision
5 diametrically
7 extermination
9 thermos
10 thrifty
12 excommunication
16 greengrocer
18 crusader
19 whey
20 sewerage
22 corkscrew
25 eucalyptus

Solutions: avion, canalizare, ciocănitoare, croitorie, cruciat, diametral, econom, ecvestru, epitet, eucalipt, excomunicare, expresionism, exterminare, favorabil, impresar, incizie, laringe, manifestant, mucegai, obtuz, piton, purtare, termos, tirbuşon, turbat, ursuz, vagabond, zarzavagiu, Zepelin, zer. (30 words). See www.websters-online-dictionary.org

Puzzle #86:   Level 1 - Just for Fun

© Philip M. Parker, INSEAD; www.websters-online-dictionary.org

Across

1 asterisk
3 dynamo
4 prodigal, spender
6 confessor
9 xenophobia
12 invocation
14 accordion
17 virtuosity
18 boatman
20 indivisible
23 tributary
25 alchemy
26 ephemeral
27 rabies
28 slave, thrall

Down

1 amphibious
2 onlooker
5 poodle
7 odyssey
8 apostrophe
10 staid, demure, earnest
11 scooter
13 asphalt
15 stilts
16 anchoret, hermit, recluse
19 renegade
21 greedy, voracious
22 sheepish, shy
23 azure
24 tonnage

Solutions: acordeon, afluent, alchimie, amfibiu, apostrof, asfalt, asterisc, azur, barcagiu, catalige, dinam, duhovnic, efemer, indivizibil, invocare, lacom, odisee, pudel, pustnic, renegat, risipitor, sclav, scuter, serios, spectator, timid, tonaj, turbare, virtuozitate, xenofobie. (30 words). See www.websters-online-dictionary.org

Puzzle #87:   Level 1 - Just for Fun

© Philip M. Parker, INSEAD; www.websters-online-dictionary.org

Across

1 chandelier
3 horned
5 spindle
8 zoology
11 atheism
13 counterpoint
15 nebulous
17 scholastic
19 liqueur
22 downcast
23 asperity, roughness
24 pseudonym
26 fission
28 balm
29 cloudless, serene
30 deformity

Down

2 ecstasy, rapture
4 bureaucrat
6 sprinkler
7 oblique, slanting
9 staid, demure, earnest
10 solemnity
12 euphemism
14 nothingness
16 pulley
18 fickle, whimsical
20 predicative
21 propulsion
25 layman, profane
27 virile

Solutions: asprime, ateism, balsam, birocrat, candelabru, capricios, contrapunct, cornut, deprimat, diformitate, eufemism, extaz, fisiune, fus, lichior, nebulos, nimicnicie, oblic, predicativ, profan, propulsie, pseudonim, scolastic, scripete, senin, serios, solemnitate, stropitoare, viril, zoologie. (30 words). See www.websters-online-dictionary.org

Puzzle #88:   Level 1 - Just for Fun

© Philip M. Parker, INSEAD; www.websters-online-dictionary.org

Across

3 itinerant
4 lapel
9 pus
10 oboe
14 vulgarity
15 totalitarian
17 courtier
18 mediocrity
20 encyclopedia
22 patrimony
23 fanaticism
25 longitude
27 opportunism
28 basalt
29 coachman

Down

1 oligarchy
2 parody, travesty
5 preconceived
6 manganese
7 fiend
8 innkeeper
11 ostentatious
12 imperceptible
13 peculiarity
16 couplet
19 docile
21 unobserved
24 airman
26 delirium
27 odious

Solutions: ambulant, aviator, bazalt, cuplet, curtean, delir, diavol, docil, Enciclopedie, fanatism, hangiu, imperceptibil, longitudine, mangan, mediocritate, neobservat, oboi, odios, oligarhie, oportunism, ostentativ, parodie, particularitate, patrimoniu, preconceput, puroi, rever, totalitar, vizitiu, vulgaritate. (30 words). See www.websters-online-dictionary.org

Puzzle #89: Level 1 - Just for Fun

© Philip M. Parker, INSEAD; www.websters-online-dictionary.org

Across

6 ponderous
8 ammonium
9 celluloid
10 starch
11 fluff
12 asparagus
15 ethereal
16 apparition
17 utopia
19 incoherent
22 voluptuous
23 pert, saucy
24 mercenary
26 sorrel
27 precocious
28 harlequin
29 affable, amiable, obliging
30 quizzical

Down

1 kaleidoscope
2 barbarian
3 diminutive
4 flirtation
5 artful, wily
7 rhinoceros
13 spaniel
14 inhabitant
18 irreducible
20 ointment
21 flabby
25 chromium

Solutions: alifie, amabil, amidon, amoniu, arlechin, barbar, caleidoscop, celuloid, crom, diminutiv, eteric, flasc, flirt, greoi, incoerent, ireductibil, ironic, locuitor, mercenar, obraznic, precoce, prepelicar, puf, rinocer, Roib, sparanghel, utopie, vedenie, viclean, voluptos. (30 words). See www.websters-online-dictionary.org

94

Puzzle #90:   Level 1 - Just for Fun

© Philip M. Parker, INSEAD; www.websters-online-dictionary.org

Across

2 mirage
5 greenish
6 chaste
7 genocide
9 autopsy
11 amphitheatre
16 pattern, sitter
17 kangaroo
19 calculation, calculus
21 unremitting
22 vampire
24 narration
25 stalwart
26 rheumatism
27 consulate

Down

1 proletarian
2 prodigy
3 migratory
4 nickel
5 vassal
8 dictation
10 leek
12 imperious
13 derogatory
14 mediaeval
15 indistinct
17 color
18 heredity
20 sapphire
23 ostrich

Solutions: amfiteatru, autopsie, calcul, Cangur, cast, consulat, Culoare, dictare, ereditate, genocid, imperios, medieval, migrator, minune, miraj, model, neclar, nichel, peiorativ, perseverent, praz, proletar, relatare, reumatism, robust, safir, struț, vampir, vasal, verzui. (30 words). See www.websters-online-dictionary.org

Puzzle #91:   Level 1 - Just for Fun

© Philip M. Parker, INSEAD; www.websters-online-dictionary.org

Across

2 trowel
4 tripod
5 quits
8 elliptical
13 purgatory
14 leech
16 grapefruit
19 concave
20 irregularity
21 outcast
23 plaid
24 jasmine
26 succinct
27 canine
28 perfunctory

Down

1 uninhabited
3 electrode
6 foray
7 fastidious
9 millet
10 sucker
11 pallor
12 venereal
15 tenacious
17 thermostat
18 informer
19 cypress
21 passive, quiescent
22 benzene
25 gaseous

Solutions: benzen, canin, Chiparos, chit, concav, electrod, eliptic, gazos, Grepfrut, iasomie, incursiune, informator, lipitoare, mei, mistrie, mofturos, nelocuit, neregularitate, paloare, pasiv, Pled, proscris, purgatoriu, succint, sugar, superficial, tenace, termostat, Trepied, veneric. (30 words). See www.websters-online-dictionary.org

Puzzle #92:   Level 1 - Just for Fun

Across

1 harpsichord
5 lethargy
8 purposely
10 brevity
12 poplar
13 nobleman
15 epitaph

19 surrealism
20 chastity
24 hurricane, tornado
26 hospitable
27 billion, trillion
28 heroism
29 cowardice

Down

2 motley, promiscuous
3 feline
4 pathos
6 pang, twinge
7 acne
9 nitric
11 snobbery

12 slipper
14 disorderly, riotous
16 trilogy
17 shoemaker
18 atrocious
21 synonym
22 navel
23 movable
25 fibrous

Solutions: acnee, amestecat, atroce, azotic, Bilion, buric, castitate, cizmar, clavecin, concizie, dinadins, epitaf, eroism, felin, fibros, junghi, laşitate, letargie, mobil, nobil, ospitalier, papuc, patos, plop, sinonim, snobism, suprarealism, trilogie, turbulent, uragan. (30 words). See www.websters-online-dictionary.org

Puzzle #93:   Level 1 - Just for Fun

© Philip M. Parker, INSEAD; www.websters-online-dictionary.org

Across

1 drugstore, pharmacy
5 beaver
7 adventurer
9 opportunist
11 avoidable
13 custodian
17 piracy
18 posthumous
21 indigestion
23 snout
24 blizzard
25 furrow, line
28 typist
29 disciple
30 suffix

Down

2 hypocrite
3 concise, terse
4 shutter
6 conqueror
8 bearable
10 incurable
12 venomous
14 enormity
15 astrology
16 archipelago
19 monsoon
20 raven
22 virtuoso
26 unfaithful
27 gait

Solutions: arhipelag, astrologie, aventurier, bot, castor, concis, corb, cuceritor, custode, dactilograf, discipol, enormitate, evitabil, Farmacie, incurabil, Indigestie, infidel, ipocrit, mers, muson, oblon, oportunist, piraterie, postum, rid, sufix, suportabil, veninos, virtuos, viscol. (30 words). See www.websters-online-dictionary.org

Puzzle #94: Level 1 - Just for Fun

© Philip M. Parker, INSEAD; www.websters-online-dictionary.org

Across

1 mystic
6 irrevocable
9 zoological
11 pedagogy
14 subway
15 nakedness
17 delinquent
18 supposition
21 palpable
22 ether
24 reprisals
25 slime
27 watchman
28 fragility
29 scrupulous
30 medley

Down

2 spinach
3 orgy
4 barter
5 disorderly
7 reverie
8 distillation
10 laurel
12 nudge
13 degeneration
16 nautical
19 rationalism
20 wad
23 astronomer
26 crane, winch

Solutions: amestec, astronom, degenerare, delincvent, dezordonat, distilare, eter, fragilitate, ghiont, goliciune, irevocabil, laur, macara, metrou, mistic, nautic, noroi, orgie, palpabil, paznic, pedagogie, presupunere, raţionalism, represalii, scrupulos, spanac, tampon, troc, visare, zoologic. (30 words). See www.websters-online-dictionary.org

Puzzle #95: Level 1 - Just for Fun

© Philip M. Parker, INSEAD; www.websters-online-dictionary.org

Across

1 preposterous
3 mauve
7 immorality
8 bridegroom
15 layer, stratum
16 submissive
18 artisan
19 predicate
22 propeller
23 thistle
26 constabulary
27 categorical
29 incapacity

Down

2 solidity
4 voluminous
5 patriarch
6 reciprocity
9 teller
10 sedentary
11 encore
12 thermometer
13 blasphemy
14 equatorial
17 wistful
19 averse
20 dowry
21 methodical
24 seduction
25 figurative
28 reindeer

Solutions: absurd, artizan, bis, blasfemie, categoric, ciulin, ecuatorial, Elice, farmec, figurat, imoralitate, incapacitate, jandarmerie, melancolic, metodic, mire, mov, patriarh, potrivnic, povestitor, predicat, reciprocitate, ren, sedentar, soliditate, strat, supus, termometru, voluminos, zestre. (30 words). See www.websters-online-dictionary.org

Puzzle #96:   Level 1 - Just for Fun

© Philip M. Parker, INSEAD; www.websters-online-dictionary.org

Across

4 infallible
7 homicide
10 chimpanzee
11 penniless
12 exertion
17 desertion
20 sonnet
21 ebony
22 trump
23 barometer
26 shroud
27 porous
28 perceptible
29 assignee
30 linguist

Down

1 allusion
2 thorny
3 forked
5 inactivity
6 cashier
8 mascara
9 accessory
13 cedar
14 iceberg
15 uterus
16 monotony
18 eel
19 transverse
24 prologue
25 thyme

Solutions: abanos, accesoriu, Aisberg, aluzie, atu, barometru, bifurcat, casier, cedru, cesionar, cimbru, cimpanzeu, dezertare, exercitare, giulgiu, inactivitate, infailibil, lefter, lingvist, monotonie, omucidere, perceptibil, poros, prolog, rimel, sonet, spinos, țipar, transversal, uter. (30 words). See www.websters-online-dictionary.org

Puzzle #97: Level 1 - Just for Fun

© Philip M. Parker, INSEAD; www.websters-online-dictionary.org

Across

5 veneer
6 sanitation
12 soot
13 passivity
14 waltz
17 trajectory
19 plywood
20 flea
21 gunner
23 mime
24 annals
25 ruddy
27 gaiety, mirth
28 bazaar
29 monograph

Down

1 axle
2 autograph
3 gable
4 humanism
7 utopian
8 sparrow
9 unprofitable
10 vanilla
11 apostle
12 bankrupt, insolvent
15 orphan
16 unbalanced
18 conceivable,
   imaginable
22 romanticism
26 lobe

Solutions: anale, apostol, autograf, bazar, dezechilibrat, falit, fronton, funingine, furnir, imaginabil, lob, mim, monografie, nerentabil, orfan, osie, pasivitate, placaj, purice, romantism, rumen, salubritate, traiectorie, tunar, umanism, utopic, vals, vanilie, veselie, vrabie. (30 words). See www.websters-online-dictionary.org

Puzzle #98:   Level 1 - Just for Fun

© Philip M. Parker, INSEAD; www.websters-online-dictionary.org

Across

2 nightingale
7 interlude
8 glossary
9 diver
15 evaporation
17 curious, inquisitive
20 theorist
26 impassable, impracticable
28 inexorable
29 psychiatry
30 inferiority

Down

1 oppressor, tyrant
3 mediocre
4 feverish
5 contagious
6 poppy
10 antipathy
11 mysticism
12 deafness
13 pilgrim
14 noxious
16 roe, spawn
18 lowly
19 cosmopolitan
21 utilitarian
22 discount, rebate
23 radish
24 wick
25 phosphorus
27 zenith

Solutions: antipatie, contagios, cosmopolit, curios, evaporare, febril, Fitil, fosfor, glosar, Icre, implacabil, impracticabil, inferioritate, interludiu, mac, mediocru, misticism, modest, nociv, pelerin, privighetoare, psihiatrie, Rabat, Ridiche, scafandru, surzenie, teoretician, tiran, utilitar, zenit. (30 words). See www.websters-online-dictionary.org

Puzzle #99: Level 1 - Just for Fun

© Philip M. Parker, INSEAD; www.websters-online-dictionary.org

Across

4 howl
7 accomplice
11 antidote
14 canonical
15 repertory
17 pessimism
23 honest, righteous
24 robber
26 sanitary
27 starboard
28 posterity

Down

1 biologist
2 orphanage
3 beige
5 disinterested
6 unanimity
8 isotope
9 clandestine
10 fad, mania
12 sundry
13 impassive, unmoved
14 quartz
16 sectarian
17 wren
18 squalor
19 senile
20 weighty
21 sociable
22 hectare
25 vineyard

Solutions: antidot, bej, biolog, canonic, cinstit, clandestin, complice, cuarţ, dezinteresat, divers, hectar, igienic, impasibil, important, izotop, jefuitor, manie, mizerie, orfelinat, pesimism, Pitulice, posteritate, repertoriu, sectar, senil, sociabil, tribord, unanimitate, urlet, vie. (30 words). See www.websters-online-dictionary.org

Puzzle #100:   Level 1 - Just for Fun

© Philip M. Parker, INSEAD; www.websters-online-dictionary.org

Across

3 deacon
6 harmless, innocuous
7 venerable
8 conical
9 spherical
11 graphite
13 glassy
17 phoneme
19 allegory
20 cylindrical
24 envious, jealous
25 immoral
26 equator
27 ox
28 aptitude
29 anthology
30 labyrinth

Down

1 humanist
2 clover
4 copious
5 biochemistry
10 projector
12 melon
14 espionage
15 reformer
16 sportsman
18 boulevard, avenue
21 convocation
22 pedestal
23 casino

Solutions: abundent, alegorie, antologie, aptitudine, biochimie, bou, Bulevard, Cazinou, cilindric, conic, convocare, diacon, ecuator, fonem, grafit, imoral, inofensiv, invidios, labirint, Pepene, piedestal, proiector, reformator, sferic, spionaj, sportiv, sticlos, trifoi, umanist, venerabil. (30 words). See www.websters-online-dictionary.org

Solutions

Puzzle #1. Across: 2. good = bun, 5. two = doi, 9. here = aici, 10. old = vechi, 11. five = cinci, 13. night = Noapte, 15. now = Acum, 16. four = patru, 19. we = Noi, 20. with = Cu, 21. all = tot, 22. year = an, 23. he = El, 25. not = Nu. **Down:** 1. in = în, 3. where = Unde, 4. very = Foarte, 6. money = bani, 7. and = şi, 8. time = Timp, 11. how = Cum, 12. head = cap, 13. new = nou, 14. three = trei, 17. there = acolo, 18. one = unu, 20. who = Cine, 24. long = lung.

Puzzle #2. Across: 2. from = de, 3. water = apă, 5. this = acest, 8. man = om, 10. on = pe, 11. only = numai, 14. back = Spate, 15. or = Sau, 16. what = ce, 17. six = şase, 19. through = prin, 21. under = sub, 22. their = lor, 23. day = Zi, 24. when = când. **Down:** 1. government = Guvern, 2. yes = Da, 3. other = alt, 4. which = care, 6. you = voi, 7. some = nişte, 9. she = Ea, 10. for = Pentru, 12. small = mic, 13. up = sus, 18. help = Ajutor, 20. nothing = nimic, 25. but = Dar.

Puzzle #3. Across: 4. left = stânga, 8. many = mulţi, 11. have = avea, 12. our = noastre, 13. down = jos, 15. able = capabil, 17. hand = mână, 18. something = ceva, 20. point = Punct, 21. world = lume, 22. know = şti, 24. these = aceste, 25. that = acel, 27. then = Apoi. **Down:** 1. work = funcţiona, 2. about = despre, 3. if = dacă, 5. group = Grup, 6. well = bine, 7. among = între, 9. people = oameni, 10. come = veni, 14. be = fi, 16. thing = Lucru, 17. much = mult, 18. as = Ca, 19. see = vedea, 20. over = Peste, 23. already = deja, 26. at = La.

Puzzle #4. Across: 7. development = Dezvoltare, 8. affair = afacere, 10. children = Copii, 11. nevertheless = totuşi, 12. school = şcoală, 14. far = Departe, 16. frequently = adesea, 17. name = Nume, 18. woman = femeie, 19. system = sistem, 20. life = viaţă, 21. road = Drum, 23. each = Fiecare, 26. house = casă, 28. number = număr. **Down:** 1. different = diferit, 2. right = Dreapta, 3. although = deşi, 4. council = consiliu, 5. fact = Fapt, 6. as = deoarece, 9. power = Putere, 13. case = caz, 15. room = cameră, 17. national = naţional, 19. say = spune, 22. make = face, 24. again = iar, 25. white = alb, 27. take = lua.

Puzzle #5. Across: 1. north = nord, 6. always = totdeauna, 7. free = Liber, 8. war = război, 9. voice = voce, 12. father = tată, 13. today = azi, 15. love = Dragoste, 16. ten = zece, 21. car = vagon, 22. among = Printre, 23. south = sud, 25. available = disponibil, 26. certain = sigur, 27. order = ordine, 28. full = plin, 29. open = deschis, 30. mother = mamă. **Down:** 2. round = rotund, 3. million = Milion, 4. question = întrebare, 5. law = Lege, 10. book = carte, 11. black = Negru, 14. court = Tribunal, 17. body = Corp, 18. view = Vedere, 19. child = copil, 20. above = Deasupra, 24. death = Moarte.

Puzzle #6. Across: 1. someone = cineva, 4. friend = Prieten, 6. eight = opt, 9. west = vest, 10. outcome = rezultat, 12. future = viitor, 14. air = Aer, 15. almost = Aproape, 17. century = secol, 19. bed = pat, 20. felt = fetru, 22. run = alerga, 24. early = Devreme, 25. therefore = deci, 27. read = citi, 28. yesterday = Ieri. **Down:** 2. authority = Autoritate, 3. try = încerca, 5. history = Istorie, 7. price = preţ, 8. wife = soţie, 11. language = limbă, 13. seven = şapte, 16. so = aşa, 18. city = oraş, 19. strong = puternic, 20. kind = fel, 21. sometimes = uneori, 23. east = est, 26. herself = se.

Puzzle #7. Across: 1. word = cuvînt, 4. music = muzică, 5. meeting = întâlnire, 6. short = scurt, 7. quality = Calitate, 9. call = chema, 10. adage = proverb, 12. village = Sat, 13. big = mare, 15. fish = peşte, 17. son = fiu, 20. play = juca, 21. ask = întreba, 22. committee = comitet, 23. fire = foc, 25. certainly = desigur, 26. red = roşu, 27. close = închide, 28. role = rol. **Down:** 2. understand = înţelege, 3. hospital = spital, 4. move = mişca, 8. common = islaz, 11. king = rege, 14. bring = aduce, 16. hundred = sută, 18. tax = impozit, 19. value = valoare, 24. game = joc, 25. hard = dur.

Puzzle #8. Across: 1. hair = păr, 4. field = Teren, 7. hear = auzi, 8. royal = regal, 9. light = lumină, 12. heart = inimă, 13. thousand = Mie, 14. park = parc, 17. account = cont, 20. stop = oprire, 22. lead = plumb, 23. letter = scrisoare, 24. husband = soţ, 25. lost = pierdut, 26. below = Dedesubt. **Down:** 1. maybe = poate, 2. rose = trandafir, 3. subject = subiect, 4. technology = tehnologie, 5. space = spaţiu, 6. basis = fundament, 10. oil = Ulei, 11. art = artă, 15. chapter = capitol, 16. speak = vorbi, 18. force = forţa, 19. happy = fericit, 21. risk = risc, 22. wall = perete, 24. advice = sfat.

Puzzle #9. Across: 3. Friday = vineri, 5. tea = Ceai, 7. hour = oră, 10. blood = sânge, 11. green = verde, 13. hold = ţine, 14. sound = sunet, 15. thank = mulţumi, 20. county = comitat, 21. beginning = început, 23. Monday = luni, 25. storey = etaj, 26. sun = soare, 27. anyway = oricum, 28. heavy = greu, 29. straight = drept. **Down:** 1. nor = nici, 2. amount = cantitate, 4. floor = Podea, 6. attention = atenţie, 8. science = ştiinţă, 9. wrong = greşit, 10. write = scrie, 12. unit = element, 16. human = uman, 17. theory = teorie, 18. helpful = util, 19. hall = Hol, 22. loss = pierdere, 24. easy = uşor.

Puzzle #10. Across: 3. football = fotbal, 6. chair = Scaun, 7. cold = rece, 8. glass = Pahar, 9. tree = copac, 12. bridge = pod, 18. twelve = Doisprezece, 19. newspaper = ziar, 20. ball = minge, 22. forty = patruzeci, 24. warm = cald, 25. thirty = treizeci, 26. train = tren, 27. leg = picior. **Down:** 1. brother = frate, 2. star = stea, 3. beautiful = frumos, 4. horse = cal, 5. equipment =

ECHIPAMENT, 8. rain = ploaie, 10. bus = autobuz, 11. coffee = cafea, 13. eye = ochi, 14. bear = urs, 15. wood = lemn, 16. fifty = Cincizeci, 17. arm = braț, 21. wine = vin, 22. skin = piele, 23. dry = uscat.

Puzzle #11. Across: 3. sleep = dormi, 6. audience = public, 7. forest = pădure, 10. blue = albastru, 13. brown = maro, 14. slowly = încet, 15. studio = atelier, 16. ring = Inel, 17. museum = Muzeu, 18. quarter = Sfert, 20. wind = vânt, 23. weight = Greutate, 24. gold = aur, 26. key = cheie, 28. engine = motor, 30. pain = durere. **Down:** 1. fifteen = Cincisprezece, 2. rich = bogat, 4. stone = piatră, 5. drink = bea, 8. male = Masculin, 9. mouth = gură, 11. weather = Vreme, 12. correct = corect, 19. hot = fierbinte, 21. box = Cutie, 22. wide = larg, 25. expensive = scump, 27. dog = câine, 29. river = râu.

Puzzle #12. Across: 2. goal = scop, 5. seat = Loc, 8. nobody = nimeni, 10. Sunday = Duminică, 11. daughter = fiică, 12. speaker = vorbitor, 13. birth = naștere, 14. effective = eficace, 17. soft = Moale, 18. alone = singur, 22. degree = grad, 23. sit = ședea, 25. statement = declarație, 26. empty = gol, 27. peace = pace. **Down:** 1. danger = Pericol, 3. walk = plimba, 4. change = schimb, 6. middle = Mijloc, 7. western = occidental, 9. thin = subțire, 13. trouble = necaz, 15. clean = curat, 16. fast = Repede, 17. tomorrow = mâine, 19. ready = gata, 20. physical = fizic, 21. hill = Deal, 22. neck = gât, 24. attack = Atac.

Puzzle #13. Across: 4. married = conjugal, 5. kitchen = bucătărie, 8. begin = începe, 9. daily = zilnic, 10. blacksmith = fierar, 11. corner = colț, 17. mark = semn, 18. insurance = asigurare, 19. debate = dezbatere, 23. clothes = haine, 25. kingdom = regat, 26. technical = tehnic, 27. meaning = sens, 28. budget = Buget, 29. message = Mesaj. **Down:** 1. additional = suplimentar, 2. gas = gaz, 3. crime = Delict, 5. check = bon, 6. prison = închisoare, 7. dear = drag, 12. length = lungime, 13. match = chibrit, 14. possibility = posibilitate, 15. somewhere = undeva, 16. truth = adevăr, 20. impact = ciocnire, 21. average = Medie, 22. send = trimite, 24. fear = frică.

Puzzle #14. Across: 2. sentence = propoziție, 3. historian = istoric, 6. pair = pereche, 8. unemployment = șomaj, 11. ample = suficient, 13. quiet = liniștit, 14. southern = sudic, 15. background = fond, 16. copy = exemplar, 18. equal = egal, 20. driver = șofer, 21. forget = uita, 24. object = obiect, 26. thanks = mulțumiri, 28. travel = călătorie, 29. felicitous = potrivit. **Down:** 1. source = izvor, 4. gain = câștig, 5. dangerous = periculos, 7. safe = seif, 9. elsewhere = aiurea, 10. patient = pacient, 12. bottom = Fund, 17. mental = mintal, 19. belief = credință, 22. usual = obișnuit, 23. package = colet, 25. jack = cric, 26. die = muri, 27. hell = iad.

Puzzle #15. Across: 1. smoke = fum, 5. lake = lac, 6. nose = nas, 8. airport = aeroport, 10. ear = ureche, 11. knee = genunchi, 14. mountain = munte, 15. Thursday = joi, 17. tent = cort, 19. ticket = bilet, 20. bone = os, 21. milk = lapte, 23. salt = sare, 25. owner = proprietar, 26. yellow = galben, 28. egg = ou. **Down:** 1. liver = ficat, 2. flower = floare, 3. Wednesday = miercuri, 4. coal = cărbune, 7. chest = piept, 9. rice = orez, 12. sky = Cer, 13. narrow = îngust, 16. eighty = optzeci, 17. meat = Carne, 18. sand = nisip, 22. pig = porc, 24. beer = bere, 27. lion = leu.

Puzzle #16. Across: 5. dirty = murdar, 8. silver = argint, 9. clock = ceas, 10. dress = rochie, 12. snake = șarpe, 14. eighteen = Optsprezece, 15. butter = unt, 16. bedroom = dormitor, 17. pencil = creion, 22. iron = fier, 23. garlic = usturoi, 25. oxygen = oxigen, 27. cloud = nor, 28. eleven = Unsprezece. **Down:** 1. cemetery = cimitir, 2. butterfly = fluture, 3. luggage = bagaj, 4. eagle = vultur, 6. envelope = plic, 7. valley = vale, 9. waiter = chelner, 11. rabbit = iepure, 13. pocket = buzunar, 16. tooth = dinte, 18. elephant = elefant, 19. fox = vulpe, 20. author = autor, 21. desk = Birou, 24. tiger = tigru, 26. sheep = Oaie.

Puzzle #17. Across: 2. cattle = Vite, 7. sick = bolnav, 8. dust = praf, 10. tennis = tenis, 11. cheek = obraz, 13. thirteen = treisprezece, 17. moon = lună, 18. sweet = dulce, 19. snow = zăpadă, 21. fishing = pescuit, 24. smooth = neted, 26. tower = Turn, 27. thick = gros, 28. fruit = fruct, 29. uncle = unchi. **Down:** 1. weak = slab, 3. grass = iarbă, 4. bath = Baie, 5. arrival = sosire, 6. fourteen = Paisprezece, 9. coat = palton, 11. glasses = ochelari, 12. wave = val, 14. entrance = intrare, 15. chemistry = chimie, 16. circle = cerc, 20. departure = plecare, 22. mouse = șoarece, 23. wet = ud, 25. sharp = ascuțit.

Puzzle #18. Across: 2. forehead = frunte, 4. velvet = Catifea, 8. triangle = triunghi, 10. battery = baterie, 12. menu = meniu, 13. barn = Hambar, 15. bat = liliac, 17. elbow = cot, 20. pepper = piper, 21. honey = miere, 22. potato = Cartof, 23. flag = steag, 24. wolf = lup, 25. boxing = box, 26. architect = arhitect. **Down:** 1. thou = tu, 3. button = nasture, 5. advertisement = anunț, 6. hammer = ciocan, 7. glue = Clei, 8. theater = teatru, 9. porter = hamal, 11. kidney = rinichi, 14. barrel = Butoi, 16. rainbow = curcubeu, 18. nephew = nepot, 19. deer = cerb, 20. towel = Prosop, 21. lamb = miel, 23. rat = șobolan.

Puzzle #19. Across: 3. tired = obosit, 5. gallery = galerie, 7. sugar = zahăr, 9. musical = muzical, 10. drawing = desen, 11. bishop = nebun, 14. noise = Zgomot, 15. shop = Magazin, 17. cheap = ieftin, 19. paint = vopsea, 21. landscape = peisaj, 23. photograph = fotografie, 25. customer = client, 26. philosophy = filozofie, 27. throw = arunca. **Down:** 1. bird = pasăre, 2. smell = Miros, 4. painting = tablou, 6. comfort = Confort, 8. wing = aripă, 9. Tuesday = Marți, 12. crew = Echipaj, 13. dance = Dans, 16. brain = Creier, 18. gift = Cadou, 20. finger = deget, 21. platform = peron, 22. deaf = surd, 24. cat = pisică, 25. courtyard = Curte.

Puzzle #20. Across: 3. engineer = inginer, 5. pen = toc, 9. passenger = Pasager, 10. salmon = Somon, 11. counter = tejghea, 14. priest = Preot, 15. courage = curaj, 18. farmer = fermier, 19. tourist = turist, 20. belt = Curea, 21. movie = film, 22. brush =

perie, 25. pan = Tigaie, 26. psychology = psihologie, 28. rope = Funie, 29. baker = brutar. **Down:** 1. trousers = pantaloni, 2. fat = grăsime, 4. dollar = dolar, 6. tail = coadă, 7. illegal = ilegal, 8. crystal = Cristal, 12. happiness = fericire, 13. grandfather = bunic, 16. burn = arde, 17. dictionary = dicţionar, 19. waist = talie, 23. remainder = rest, 24. colleague = coleg, 27. chaos = haos.

Puzzle #21. Across: 1. jealous = gelos, 3. cow = vacă, 5. skull = craniu, 8. lobby = vestibul, 10. oak = stejar, 13. communism = comunism, 15. vacuum = vid, 16. horn = corn, 17. fist = pumn, 18. knight = Cavaler, 19. thunder = tunet, 21. custom = Obicei, 23. photographer = fotograf, 25. tourism = turism, 27. divinity = teologie, 28. cylinder = cilindru. **Down:** 1. collar = Guler, 2. librarian = bibliotecar, 4. oven = Cuptor, 6. aquarium = Acvariu, 7. corn = Porumb, 9. ballet = Balet, 11. hydrogen = hidrogen, 12. hospitality = ospitalitate, 14. swim = înota, 17. shoe = pantof, 20. threshold = prag, 22. basket = coş, 24. tobacco = tutun, 26. juice = suc.

Puzzle #22. Across: 6. calf = viţel, 8. stool = Taburet, 9. dolphin = delfin, 10. freeze = îngheţa, 12. dragon = Balaur, 13. wallet = Portofel, 14. kite = zmeu, 16. barley = orz, 17. musician = muzician, 20. seaside = litoral, 21. skeleton = schelet, 24. nylon = Nailon, 25. screen = ecran, 27. guide = ghid, 28. parcel = pachet, 29. jockey = jocheu. **Down:** 1. catch = prinde, 2. wonderful = minunat, 3. lime = var, 4. armchair = fotoliu, 5. debt = datorie, 7. cardboard = carton, 11. jealousy = gelozie, 15. physician = medic, 17. donkey = măgar, 18. flight = zbor, 19. archaeology = arheologie, 22. cough = tuse, 23. bean = fasole, 26. nail = Cui.

Puzzle #23. Across: 1. glad = bucuros, 5. extensive = vast, 6. approval = aprobare, 7. valuable = valoros, 9. hole = gaură, 10. somewhat = cam, 12. corridor = coridor, 14. culpable = vinovat, 15. sequence = succesiune, 17. fortunate = norocos, 19. reader = cititor, 20. cove = individ, 23. engineering = inginerie, 26. maintenance = întreţinere, 27. massive = masiv, 28. dream = vis. **Down:** 2. subsequent = ulterior, 3. flat = apartament, 4. lead = conducere, 7. revenue = venit, 8. somehow = cumva, 11. roof = acoperiş, 13. file = Dosar, 16. youth = Tineret, 18. sixty = şaizeci, 21. taste = gust, 22. flow = curge, 23. vast = imens, 24. unique = unic, 25. ourselves = ne.

Puzzle #24. Across: 3. push = împinge, 6. stick = baston, 8. aunt = mătuşă, 9. duke = duce, 10. golden = auriu, 11. empire = imperiu, 14. bell = clopot, 16. enemy = duşman, 17. chain = lanţ, 22. ice = gheaţă, 24. equivalent = echivalent, 25. achievement = realizare, 27. parish = parohie, 28. idea = idee. **Down:** 1. suggestion = sugestie, 2. namely = anume, 4. fly = muscă, 5. visual = vizual, 7. writer = scriitor, 9. trained = dresat, 12. gruff = aspru, 13. dish = farfurie, 15. chancellor = cancelar, 16. fault = defect, 18. defendant = acuzat, 19. decade = deceniu, 20. pollution = poluare, 21. objective = obiectiv, 23. rent = chirie, 26. steel = oţel.

Puzzle #25. Across: 1. surgery = chirurgie, 7. tank = Tanc, 9. kiss = sărut, 10. barely = doar, 11. split = despica, 14. expert = specialist, 16. seventy = şaptezeci, 18. plaintiff = reclamant, 19. jury = juriu, 20. joy = bucurie, 21. wan = palid, 23. visible = vizibil, 25. mission = misiune, 27. luck = noroc, 29. register = înregistra. **Down:** 2. phrase = expresie, 3. equation = ecuaţie, 4. mummy = mumie, 5. communist = comunist, 6. cruel = crud, 8. shirt = cămaşă, 12. sixteen = şaisprezece, 13. knife = cuţit, 15. ceiling = Tavan, 17. discovery = descoperire, 22. destruction = distrugere, 24. cotton = bumbac, 25. mechanism = mecanism, 26. poem = poezie, 28. hate = urî.

Puzzle #26. Across: 4. unfair = nedrept, 6. scientist = savant, 9. carpet = covor, 10. tin = cositor, 11. hero = erou, 13. tissue = ţesut, 14. miller = Morar, 16. addition = Adunare, 20. tunnel = tunel, 21. unhappy = nefericit, 24. mystery = mister, 25. root = rădăcină, 26. guardian = tutore, 28. summary = rezumat, 29. anywhere = oriunde. **Down:** 1. anniversary = aniversare, 2. phenomenon = fenomen, 3. cheque = cec, 5. reception = primire, 7. barrister = avocat, 8. conviction = condamnare, 12. friendship = prietenie, 15. storm = furtună, 17. withdrawal = retragere, 18. lesson = lecţie, 19. cigarette = ţigară, 22. bitter = amar, 23. apple = măr, 24. witness = martor, 27. ford = Vad.

Puzzle #27. Across: 2. seventeen = şaptesprezece, 4. neighbour = vecin, 5. correspondent = corespondent, 6. mayor = primar, 8. merchant = comerciant, 10. isolation = izolare, 13. chronic = cronic, 14. appendix = apendice, 19. monthly = lunar, 20. dull = bont, 21. resigned = resemnat, 22. fence = Gard, 23. chicken = Pui, 24. systematic = sistematic, 26. reign = domnie, 27. lover = iubit, 28. example = exemplu. **Down:** 1. forgiveness = iertare, 2. symbol = simbol, 3. therapy = terapie, 5. chemical = chimic, 7. scarcely = abia, 9. manufacturer = fabricant, 11. commander = comandant, 12. cousin = văr, 15. equity = echitate, 16. pipe = tub, 17. suicide = sinucidere, 18. abode = domiciliu, 25. bank = mal.

Puzzle #28. Across: 1. forum = for, 8. dynamic = dinamic, 11. prior = anterior, 13. dean = Decan, 14. lily = Crin, 16. indefinite = vag, 19. pond = iaz, 24. super = figurant, 26. tournament = turnir, 27. racial = rasial, 28. publisher = editor, 29. equilibrium = echilibru. **Down:** 2. hostile = ostil, 3. orange = portocală, 4. bull = Taur, 5. liquid = lichid, 6. myth = mit, 7. anyone = oricine, 9. avenue = Alee, 10. manor = conac, 12. seed = sămânţă, 15. rejection = respingere, 17. applicable = aplicabil, 18. adviser = consilier, 19. hierarchy = ierarhie, 20. rhythm = ritm, 21. eager = dornic, 22. vessel = vas, 23. deck = punte, 25. hard = tare.

Puzzle #29. Across: 1. crude = brut, 3. shelf = Raft, 6. archbishop = arhiepiscop, 7. copper = cupru, 10. equality = egalitate, 11. leaf = frunză, 13. to = spre, 14. inn = han, 16. journalist = ziarist, 17. inherent = inerent, 18. lorry = camion, 21. validity = valabilitate, 22. eve = ajun, 23. bloke = tip, 25. drunk = beat, 26. skilled = calificat, 27. loyal = loial, 28. unacceptable =

inacceptabil. **Down:** 2. terror = teroare, 4. pavement = trotuar, 5. sovereignty = suveranitate, 8. striker = grevist, 9. butler = Majordom, 12. hostility = ostilitate, 15. appreciation = apreciere, 19. unavailing = inutil, 20. honourable = onorabil, 24. curtain = perdea, 25. dioxide = bioxid, 26. nest = Cuib.

Puzzle #30. Across: 1. foolish = prostesc, 7. luxury = lux, 8. jazz = jaz, 13. coherent = coerent, 14. abortion = avorton, 15. erosion = eroziune, 16. cheerful = voios, 20. stamp = Timbru, 23. bass = bas, 24. lid = Capac, 25. hunger = foame, 27. throne = tron, 28. rod = vergea, 30. territorial = teritorial. **Down:** 2. subjective = subiectiv, 3. gravy = sos, 4. ash = frasin, 5. fury = furie, 6. polytechnic = politehnic, 9. ferry = bac, 10. bile = fiere, 11. sweat = transpiraţie, 12. shy = ruşinos, 17. helicopter = elicopter, 18. orthodox = ortodox, 19. tenth = zecime, 21. gradual = treptat, 22. apparatus = aparat, 26. cooper = Dogar, 29. needle = Ac.

Puzzle #31. Across: 1. loving = iubitor, 5. stunning = splendid, 6. trophy = trofeu, 8. noisy = zgomotos, 10. couch = Canapea, 13. artist = pictor, 15. presently = imediat, 18. yacht = iaht, 19. vivid = viu, 21. trainer = antrenor, 22. bad = prost, 24. graph = grafic, 26. vocational = profesional, 27. lieutenant = locotenent, 28. cage = colivie, 29. methodology = metodologie. **Down:** 1. immune = imun, 2. exit = ieşire, 3. drawer = sertar, 4. owl = bufniţă, 7. folly = Nebunie, 9. surgeon = chirurg, 11. against = contra, 12. fog = ceaţă, 14. immigration = imigrare, 16. optional = facultativ, 17. domain = domeniu, 20. nuisance = pacoste, 23. choir = cor, 25. slice = Felie.

Puzzle #32. Across: 1. ally = aliat, 4. maid = servitoare, 5. rotten = putred, 8. recorder = magnetofon, 10. lazy = leneş, 13. asylum = refugiu, 15. imminent = iminent, 16. accountant = contabil, 17. frost = ger, 18. debtor = datornic, 21. mankind = omenire, 26. builder = constructor, 27. surgical = chirurgical, 28. bicycle = bicicletă, 29. telly = televizor. **Down:** 2. assertion = afirmare, 3. steal = fura, 5. feasible = posibil, 6. ruler = domnitor, 7. trustee = administrator, 9. whichever = oricare, 11. highway = şosea, 12. pine = pin, 14. squadron = escadron, 19. amnesty = amnistie, 20. accompany = însoţi, 22. deadly = mortal, 23. parking = parcare, 24. corpse = cadavru, 25. reed = Stuf.

Puzzle #33. Across: 5. communal = comunal, 6. jam = Gem, 9. damned = blestemat, 11. unstable = instabil, 12. denial = negare, 14. boil = fierbe, 16. debris = moloz, 17. siege = asediu, 21. prediction = prezicere, 22. creed = crez, 24. symmetry = simetrie, 25. robbery = jaf, 26. float = pluti, 27. calumny = calomnie, 28. cherry = cireaşă, 29. notebook = Blocnotes, 30. cruelty = cruzime. **Down:** 1. honorary = onorific, 2. irregular = neregulat, 3. fork = furculiţă, 4. authentic = autentic, 7. quantum = cuantum, 8. terrorist = terorist, 10. ski = schiu, 13. applicant = solicitant, 15. swallow = rândunică, 18. inequality = inegalitate, 19. cellular = celular, 20. wording = formulare, 23. synthetic = sintetic.

Puzzle #34. Across: 2. admiral = amiral, 5. substantive = independent, 7. volcanic = vulcanic, 10. desert = pustiu, 14. hearsay = zvon, 15. residual = rezidual, 17. impetus = impuls, 19. rosemary = Rozmarin, 20. thief = hoţ, 21. balloon = Balon, 22. acre = acru, 23. terrorism = terorism, 26. ax = topor, 27. renowned = renumit, 28. fussy = agitat, 29. onion = ceapă, 30. quotation = citat. **Down:** 1. pathetic = patetic, 3. knot = nod, 4. pony = ponei, 6. robust = viguros, 8. gospel = evanghelie, 9. mosaic = mozaic, 11. saddle = şa, 12. honesty = cinste, 13. overseer = supraveghetor, 16. cement = ciment, 18. passport = paşaport, 24. tomato = roşie, 25. selfish = egoist.

Puzzle #35. Across: 1. pitiless = nemilos, 2. inner = interior, 5. clinging = colant, 8. resistant = rezistent, 9. screw = şurub, 11. anguish = chin, 13. lightning = fulger, 16. dusk = amurg, 20. picturesque = pitoresc, 21. theatrical = teatral, 23. novelist = romancier, 24. qualitative = calitativ, 25. readiness = promptitudine, 26. jar = Borcan, 28. banker = bancher, 29. anthropology = antropologie. **Down:** 1. nut = nucă, 3. reservation = Rezervare, 4. sensory = senzorial, 6. glossy = lucios, 7. unofficial = neoficial, 10. sweater = Pulover, 12. immunity = imunitate, 14. cannon = tun, 15. authoritative = autoritar, 17. conquest = cucerire, 18. rub = freca, 19. donor = donator, 22. allegiance = supunere, 27. ripe = copt.

Puzzle #36. Across: 4. suitcase = geamantan, 7. goat = capră, 8. juvenile = tineresc, 10. novelty = noutate, 12. burglary = spargere, 14. intricate = complicat, 16. symptom = simptom, 17. nomination = numire, 18. mole = aluniţă, 19. bowling = Popice, 21. translate = traduce, 25. extinction = stingere, 26. philosopher = filozof, 28. heroic = eroic, 29. tyre = pneu, 30. outer = exterior. **Down:** 1. humid = umed, 2. stylistic = stilistic, 3. dancer = dansator, 5. dam = Baraj, 6. majesty = maiestate, 9. noun = substantiv, 11. advisable = recomandabil, 13. proximity = apropiere, 15. tedious = plicticos, 20. kindred = rudenie, 22. coupon = cupon, 23. astonishment = uimire, 24. hilarious = vesel, 27. potter = Olar.

Puzzle #37. Across: 5. carrot = morcov, 6. mast = catarg, 7. charcoal = mangal, 9. reef = Recif, 11. plump = durduliu, 13. bark = scoarţă, 17. fashionable = elegant, 21. lucrative = profitabil, 23. exhaustion = epuizare, 25. worm = vierme, 26. eccentric = excentric, 27. cucumber = castravete, 28. mattress = saltea, 29. dessert = Desert. **Down:** 1. refrigerator = frigider, 2. rectangle = dreptunghi, 3. sailor = marinar, 4. razor = brici, 8. alphabet = Alfabet, 10. flute = flaut, 12. pigeon = porumbel, 13. sausage = salam, 14. applause = aplauze, 15. scissors = foarfece, 16. comb = pieptene, 18. buffet = bufet, 19. elevator = lift, 20. volcano = vulcan, 22. recurrence = repetare, 24. luxurious = luxos.

Puzzle #38. Across: 1. bulb = bec, 4. chess = şah, 6. perfume = parfum, 10. bouquet = Buchet, 11. vinegar = oţet, 13. cocoa = Cacao, 14. pineapple = ananas, 17. mythology = mitologie, 18. shark = rechin, 19. cuckoo = cuc, 20. snail = melc, 24. feather = pană, 25. physiology = fiziologie, 26. rum = rom, 27. barber = frizer. **Down:** 1. sponge = burete, 2. cone = con, 3. symphony =

Simfonie, 4. symbolism = simbolism, 5. penguin = Pinguin, 6. parrot = Papagal, 7. lipstick = Ruj, 8. ashes = scrum, 9. fisherman = pescar, 12. hockey = Hochei, 15. mosque = Moschee, 16. pedestrian = Pieton, 21. necklace = colier, 22. beech = fag, 23. buffalo = bivol.

Puzzle #39. Across: 3. willow = salcie, 4. dynasty = dinastie, 8. garbage = Gunoi, 10. hypothetical = ipotetic, 11. solemn = grav, 13. pleasing = agreabil, 14. pawn = pion, 15. mortal = muritor, 17. lighthouse = Far, 19. listener = auditor, 20. massage = masaj, 21. mute = mut, 23. beak = Cioc, 24. athletics = atletism, 25. pupil = elev, 26. avoidance = evitare, 28. gifted = talentat. **Down:** 1. syrup = Sirop, 2. corporal = Caporal, 5. tsar = ţar, 6. apprentice = ucenic, 7. contingency = eventualitate, 9. swollen = umflat, 12. camouflage = Camuflaj, 14. rainy = ploios, 16. rucksack = rucsac, 18. hedgehog = arici, 21. mass = mulţime, 22. messenger = mesager, 27. thirst = sete.

Puzzle #40. Across: 2. carpenter = dulgher, 4. irresponsible = iresponsabil, 5. sleepy = somnoros, 6. chaotic = haotic, 12. homage = omagiu, 15. angular = unghiular, 18. foreman = maistru, 20. hereditary = ereditar, 21. ludicrous = ridicol, 23. hysterical = isteric, 25. phosphate = fosfat, 27. adventurous = aventuros, 28. famine = foamete, 29. ostensible = aparent, 30. ore = minereu. **Down:** 1. pilgrimage = pelerinaj, 3. extinct = mort, 7. curly = ondulat, 8. witty = spiritual, 9. earthquake = cutremur, 10. greeting = salut, 11. slavery = sclavie, 13. hideous = hidos, 14. visibility = vizibilitate, 16. freezer = Congelator, 17. skiing = Schi, 19. missionary = misionar, 22. baptism = botez, 24. mustard = muştar, 26. guts = maţe.

Puzzle #41. Across: 3. rhetorical = retoric, 5. aquatic = acvatic, 8. enlightenment = iluminism, 9. lush = luxuriant, 12. awfully = teribil, 13. homeland = patrie, 15. unavoidable = inevitabil, 16. dignified = demn, 18. almighty = atotputernic, 21. bane = nenorocire, 22. timely = oportun, 24. quarterly = trimestrial, 26. defiance = sfidare, 27. millionaire = milionar, 28. hybrid = hibrid. **Down:** 1. sod = gazon, 2. pamphlet = pamflet, 4. tailor = croitor, 6. coke = cocs, 7. psychiatrist = psihiatru, 10. roast = frige, 11. stately = falnic, 13. pleading = pledoarie, 14. glider = planor, 17. inappropriate = nepotrivit, 18. advantageous = avantajos, 19. prehistoric = preistoric, 20. gloss = luciu, 23. scar = cicatrice, 25. steam = abur.

Puzzle #42. Across: 2. sparkling = spumos, 4. quay = chei, 6. camel = cămilă, 7. unbearable = insuportabil, 13. jewel = Bijuterie, 15. benevolent = binevoitor, 17. illegitimate = nelegitim, 18. proprietary = brevetat, 21. battalion = batalion, 23. sensual = senzual, 24. drown = îneca, 26. archaic = arhaic, 29. boar = vier, 30. viscount = Viconte. **Down:** 1. dishonest = necinstit, 3. folder = pliant, 5. carp = crap, 8. lottery = loterie, 9. scarce = rar, 10. searchlight = reflector, 11. liar = mincinos, 12. prophet = profet, 14. ounce = uncie, 16. preacher = predicator, 19. explosion = izbucnire, 20. dice = Zaruri, 22. technician = tehnician, 25. athlete = atlet, 27. bud = boboc, 28. pious = pios.

Puzzle #43. Across: 2. phenomenal = fenomenal, 5. resumption = reluare, 7. stocking = ciorap, 10. jade = jad, 11. humanitarian = umanitar, 12. sleek = lins, 14. pink = roz, 15. clown = Clovn, 19. believer = credincios, 21. envoy = trimis, 23. sewing = cusut, 24. soda = sifon, 25. claimant = pretendent, 27. cider = cidru, 28. chronological = cronologic. **Down:** 1. rash = pripit, 3. lyrical = liric, 4. disapproval = dezaprobare, 6. ruby = Rubin, 7. clear = clar, 8. overweight = supragreutate, 9. paste = pap, 13. pollen = polen, 16. walnut = nuc, 17. devious = ocolit, 18. caller = vizitator, 19. exhaustive = complet, 20. indefinite = nedefinit, 22. amen = amin, 26. cube = cub.

Puzzle #44. Across: 1. strife = conflict, 2. mammal = mamifer, 10. chlorine = clor, 12. tyranny = tiranie, 13. hysteria = isterie, 14. hem = Tiv, 17. humidity = umiditate, 18. dregs = drojdie, 22. deference = respect, 24. grievous = dureros, 26. glaring = orbitor, 27. arson = incendiere, 28. coy = sfios, 29. harmonious = armonios. **Down:** 1. chronology = cronologie, 3. mechanic = mecanic, 4. hostage = ostatic, 5. overcoat = pardesiu, 6. folly = prostie, 7. intruder = nepoftit, 8. disarmament = dezarmare, 9. lesion = leziune, 11. folding = rabatabil, 15. suffrage = vot, 16. terrestrial = terestru, 19. unreal = ireal, 20. assassin = asasin, 21. yoghurt = iaurt, 23. embroidery = broderie, 25. plum = prună.

Puzzle #45. Across: 1. motorist = automobilist, 3. snack = gustare, 4. badger = bursuc, 6. softness = moliciune, 9. nasal = nazal, 10. cynicism = cinism, 13. attentive = atent, 17. null = nul, 19. spice = condiment, 20. relay = releu, 21. disadvantage = dezavantaj, 24. torrent = torent, 25. raincoat = impermeabil, 26. assortment = Asortiment, 27. deadlock = impas. **Down:** 1. topical = actual, 2. humility = smerenie, 5. blindness = orbire, 7. courier = curier, 8. dagger = pumnal, 11. plumage = penaj, 12. souvenir = Suvenir, 13. affiliation = afiliere, 14. molten = topit, 15. illicit = ilicit, 16. immortal = nemuritor, 18. hydraulic = hidraulic, 22. fat = gras, 23. spurious = fals, 25. anthem = imn.

Puzzle #46. Across: 2. mysterious = misterios, 4. bosom = suflet, 6. oblivion = uitare, 10. fuselage = fuzelaj, 12. frightful = groaznic, 14. corrosion = coroziune, 15. pore = por, 16. quaint = ciudat, 17. fluffy = pufos, 18. fugitive = fugar, 20. lobster = Homar, 24. livery = livrea, 25. stiffness = rigiditate, 29. sardonic = batjocoritor, 30. sequel = urmare. **Down:** 1. folklore = folclor, 3. extant = existent, 5. phonetic = fonetic, 7. visionary = imaginar, 8. adept = expert, 9. stag = burlac, 11. morphology = morfologie, 13. convict = condamnat, 19. workable = realizabil, 21. rabbi = rabin, 22. parchment = pergament, 23. worldly = lumesc, 26. gallop = galop, 27. thrush = sturz, 28. measles = pojar.

Puzzle #47. Across: 1. fir = brad, 3. tapestry = tapiserie, 5. sumptuous = somptuos, 8. sender = expeditor, 11. unproductive = neproductiv, 12. advantage = avantaj, 14. usher = plasator, 15. kernel = miez, 16. bookseller = librar, 20. moth = molie, 21.

canyon = Canion, 23. smoky = afumat, 24. paddock = padoc, 26. salient = proeminent, 27. frosty = geros, 28. mimic = imitator, 29. sob = suspin. **Down:** 2. inorganic = anorganic, 4. beehive = stup, 6. lantern = Felinar, 7. symposium = simpozion, 9. resilience = elasticitate, 10. commercial = comercial, 13. playwright = dramaturg, 17. occupant = ocupant, 18. sedate = calm, 19. mountainous = muntos, 22. illustrious = ilustru, 24. poker = pocher, 25. courageous = curajos.

Puzzle #48. Across: 7. plumber = instalator, 9. obituary = necrolog, 10. pitiful = milos, 11. asparagus = sparanghel, 13. allergy = Alergie, 14. snag = ciot, 16. venom = venin, 17. debatable = discutabil, 22. piquant = picant, 24. hypocrisy = ipocrizie, 25. slang = argou, 26. orchid = orhidee, 27. cashier = casier, 28. nominee = candidat. **Down:** 1. remembrance = amintire, 2. sodden = necopt, 3. uproar = vacarm, 4. knack = pricepere, 5. forlorn = nenorocit, 6. cyclist = biciclist, 7. immigrant = imigrant, 8. eatable = comestibil, 12. resilient = elastic, 15. chic = şic, 16. ship = Vapor, 18. falcon = şoim, 19. boon = favoare, 20. heresy = erezie, 21. tremor = fior, 23. treatise = tratat.

Puzzle #49. Across: 2. nightingale = privighetoare, 5. drugstore = Farmacie, 8. humanism = umanism, 10. iceberg = Aisberg, 13. poppy = mac, 14. tulip = Lalea, 17. equator = ecuator, 19. rhinoceros = rinocer, 24. spinach = spanac, 26. subway = metrou, 27. lapel = rever, 28. pheasant = Fazan, 29. thermometer = termometru. **Down:** 1. sparrow = vrabie, 3. radish = Ridiche, 4. hammock = hamac, 6. raven = corb, 7. flea = purice, 9. artichoke = anghinare, 11. boulevard = bulevard, 12. isotope = izotop, 15. oyster = stridie, 16. zipper = fermoar, 18. propeller = Elice, 20. ox = bou, 21. leek = praz, 22. melon = Pepene, 23. shutter = oblon, 24. sonnet = sonet, 25. beaver = castor.

Puzzle #50. Across: 4. starling = graur, 5. aircraft = avion, 7. harbor = Port, 8. ostrich = struţ, 9. flax = in, 11. oboe = oboi, 13. accordion = acordeon, 14. ladle = polonic, 20. etymology = etimologie, 22. poplar = plop, 23. grapefruit = Grepfrut, 25. staid = serios, 26. navel = buric, 27. shipwreck = Naufragiu, 28. marten = jder. **Down:** 1. color = Culoare, 2. kangaroo = Cangur, 3. pumpkin = Dovleac, 6. polecat = dihor, 8. shrew = scorpie, 10. encyclopedia = Enciclopedie, 12. starch = amidon, 15. liqueur = lichior, 16. skier = schior, 17. atheism = ateism, 18. suspenders = bretele, 19. hippopotamus = Hipopotam, 21. tripod = Trepied, 24. louse = păduche, 25. sled = Sanie.

Puzzle #51. Across: 4. base = josnic, 7. casino = Cazinou, 9. harmless = inofensiv, 10. spherical = sferic, 11. selfishness = egoism, 13. humanist = umanist, 16. allegory = alegorie, 18. faucet = Robinet, 21. clover = trifoi, 22. deacon = diacon, 25. opaque = opac, 26. mammoth = mamut, 27. phoneme = fonem, 28. unfriendly = neprietenos. **Down:** 1. taboo = tabu, 2. pedestal = piedestal, 3. projector = proiector, 5. glassy = sticlos, 6. sew = coase, 8. elm = ulm, 12. emerald = smarald, 14. espionage = spionaj, 15. appetizer = Aperitiv, 16. anthology = antologie, 17. graphite = grafit, 19. copious = abundent, 20. fateful = fatal, 22. stench = duhoare, 23. beefsteak = biftec, 24. juicy = zemos.

Puzzle #52. Across: 1. inexorable = implacabil, 5. sundry = divers, 8. quartz = cuarţ, 12. robber = jefuitor, 15. orphanage = orfelinat, 17. starboard = tribord, 18. immoral = imoral, 19. discount = rabat, 22. pessimism = pesimism, 23. wick = Fitil, 25. squalor = mizerie, 26. sanitary = igienic, 27. feverish = febril, 28. weighty = important. **Down:** 2. accomplice = complice, 3. beige = bej, 4. noxious = nociv, 5. disinterested = dezinteresat, 6. vineyard = vie, 7. howl = urlet, 9. deafness = surzenie, 10. envious = invidios, 11. diver = scafandru, 13. cylindrical = cilindric, 14. labyrinth = labirint, 16. pilgrim = pelerin, 17. theorist = teoretician, 20. wren = Pitulice, 21. mysticism = misticism, 24. honest = cinstit.

Puzzle #53. Across: 8. passivity = pasivitate, 10. sanitation = salubritate, 14. axle = osie, 15. thyme = cimbru, 16. phosphorus = fosfor, 21. mime = mim, 22. unbalanced = dezechilibrat, 26. unprofitable = nerentabil, 28. lowly = modest, 29. orphan = orfan, 30. plywood = placaj. **Down:** 1. soot = funingine, 2. ruddy = rumen, 3. trajectory = traiectorie, 4. shroud = giulgiu, 5. bankrupt = falit, 6. trump = atu, 7. roe = Icre, 9. waltz = vals, 11. gunner = tunar, 12. psychiatry = psihiatrie, 13. veneer = furnir, 17. lobe = lob, 18. chimpanzee = cimpanzeu, 19. gaiety = veselie, 20. oppressor = tiran, 23. cedar = cedru, 24. annals = anale, 25. gable = fronton, 27. mascara = rimel.

Puzzle #54. Across: 3. mauve = mov, 6. medley = amestec, 7. methodical = metodic, 10. immorality = imoralitate, 13. penniless = lefter, 16. forked = bifurcat, 17. assignee = cesionar, 19. dowry = zestre, 21. submissive = supus, 22. preposterous = absurd, 23. encore = bis, 24. reindeer = ren, 25. constabulary = jandarmerie, 26. teller = povestitor, 27. eel = ţipar, 28. irrevocable = irevocabil. **Down:** 1. seduction = farmec, 2. thistle = ciulin, 3. wistful = melancolic, 4. bridegroom = mire, 5. watchman = paznic, 8. orgy = orgie, 9. slime = noroi, 11. ebony = abanos, 12. equatorial = ecuatorial, 14. homicide = omucidere, 15. averse = potrivnic, 18. allusion = aluzie, 20. desertion = dezertare, 21. thorny = spinos.

Puzzle #55. Across: 2. supposition = presupunere, 5. gait = mers, 6. nakedness = goliciune, 7. snout = bot, 10. harpsichord = clavecin, 12. typist = dactilograf, 13. venomous = veninos, 16. rationalism = raţionalism, 19. ether = eter, 22. blizzard = viscol, 23. bearable = suportabil, 26. hypocrite = ipocrit, 28. adventurer = aventurier, 29. conqueror = cuceritor. **Down:** 1. archipelago = arhipelag, 3. avoidable = evitabil, 4. furrow = rid, 8. opportunist = oportunist, 9. unfaithful = infidel, 11. wad = tampon, 14. surrealism = suprarealism, 15. nobleman = nobil, 17. monsoon = muson, 18. disorderly = dezordonat, 20. suffix = sufix, 21. mystic = mistic, 22. reverie = visare, 24. crane = macara, 25. nudge = ghiont, 27. barter = troc.

Puzzle #56. Across: 2. brevity = concizie, 3. cypress = Chiparos, 5. slipper = papuc, 8. disorderly = turbulent, 10. pathos = patos, 12. elliptical = eliptic, 14. billion = Bilion, 15. nitric = azotic, 17. thermostat = termostat, 19. plaid = Pled, 22. millet = mei, 23. cowardice = lașitate, 26. irregularity = neregularitate, 27. gaseous = gazos, 28. heroism = eroism. **Down:** 1. synonym = sinonim, 4. foray = incursiune, 6. motley = amestecat, 7. sucker = sugar, 9. quits = chit, 11. hospitable = ospitalier, 13. movable = mobil, 16. shoemaker = cizmar, 18. chastity = castitate, 19. passive = pasiv, 20. purposely = dinadins, 21. lethargy = letargie, 22. fastidious = mofturos, 24. pang = junghi, 25. hurricane = uragan.

Puzzle #57. Across: 1. quizzical = ironic, 7. amphitheatre = amfiteatru, 8. outcast = proscris, 10. ethereal = eteric, 11. nickel = nichel, 12. sapphire = safir, 13. uninhabited = nelocuit, 14. trowel = mistrie, 17. greenish = verzui, 18. apparition = vedenie, 20. affable = amabil, 21. artful = viclean, 22. ponderous = greoi, 24. stalwart = robust, 25. harlequin = arlechin, 26. perfunctory = superficial. **Down:** 2. chaste = cast, 3. pallor = paloare, 4. heredity = ereditate, 5. pattern = Model, 6. leech = lipitoare, 8. unremitting = perseverent, 9. narration = relatare, 14. prodigy = minune, 15. rheumatism = reumatism, 16. derogatory = peiorativ, 19. jasmine = iasomie, 21. vassal = vasal, 23. indistinct = neclar, 24. sorrel = Roib.

Puzzle #58. Across: 1. courtier = curtean, 3. fluff = puf, 6. inhabitant = locuitor, 7. pert = obraznic, 9. fiend = diavol, 11. itinerant = ambulant, 13. basalt = bazalt, 14. chromium = crom, 17. asperity = asprime, 22. couplet = cuplet, 23. flabby = flasc, 24. irreducible = ireductibil, 25. kaleidoscope = caleidoscop, 26. ointment = alifie, 27. scholastic = scolastic, 28. spaniel = prepelicar. **Down:** 2. ammonium = amoniu, 3. pus = puroi, 4. celluloid = celuloid, 5. coachman = vizitiu, 8. innkeeper = hangiu, 10. peculiarity = particularitate, 12. nothingness = nimicnicie, 15. opportunism = oportunism, 16. chandelier = candelabru, 17. airman = aviator, 18. euphemism = eufemism, 19. counterpoint = contrapunct, 20. unobserved = neobservat, 21. cloudless = senin.

Puzzle #59. Across: 1. scooter = scuter, 3. pulley = scripete, 4. fickle = capricios, 7. rabies = turbare, 9. dynamo = dinam, 11. prodigal = risipitor, 17. ephemeral = efemer, 18. deformity = diformitate, 20. amphibious = amfibiu, 23. slave = sclav, 25. horned = cornut, 26. tonnage = tonaj, 27. tributary = afluent, 29. fission = fisiune. **Down:** 2. stilts = catalige, 5. onlooker = spectator, 6. balm = balsam, 8. bureaucrat = birocrat, 10. downcast = deprimat, 12. sprinkler = stropitoare, 13. anchoret = pustnic, 14. boatman = barcagiu, 15. confessor = duhovnic, 16. odyssey = odisee, 17. ecstasy = extaz, 19. sheepish = timid, 21. asphalt = asfalt, 22. poodle = pudel, 24. greedy = lacom, 28. spindle = fus.

Puzzle #60. Across: 2. demonstrator = manifestant, 7. vagrant = vagabond, 10. sewerage = canalizare, 12. auspicious = favorabil, 16. equestrian = ecvestru, 17. morose = ursuz, 18. manger = iesle, 20. bricklayer = zidar, 21. greengrocer = zarzavagiu, 22. locket = medalion, 26. pollination = polenizare, 27. hilarity = ilaritate, 28. iodine = iod, 29. woodpecker = ciocănitoare, 30. python = piton. **Down:** 1. tadpole = mormoloc, 3. fireman = fochist, 4. preternatural = supranatural, 5. corkscrew = tirbușon, 6. rabid = turbat, 8. crusader = cruciat, 9. whey = zer, 11. thrifty = econom, 13. zeppelin = Zepelin, 14. mildew = mucegai, 15. behavior = purtare, 19. syllabic = silabic, 23. larynx = laringe, 24. thermos = termos, 25. tailoring = croitorie.

Puzzle #61. Across: 3. scurrilous = injurios, 6. fingernail = unghie, 8. cynic = cinic, 9. jaundice = icter, 10. ochre = ocru, 11. purr = tors, 12. kayak = Caiac, 15. cyclone = ciclon, 16. belligerent = beligerant, 18. breakwater = dig, 22. penknife = briceag, 23. trachea = trahee, 24. climber = Alpinist, 25. storehouse = depozit, 26. alligator = Aligator, 28. woodcock = Sitar, 29. abstruse = ascuns, 30. prolongation = prelungire. **Down:** 1. renown = renume, 2. smallness = micime, 4. protractor = raportor, 5. throaty = gutural, 7. inaccuracy = inexactitate, 13. tyrannical = tiranic, 14. insincere = nesincer, 17. leper = lepros, 19. portly = corpolent, 20. fatality = calamitate, 21. servitude = robie, 27. laziness = lene.

Puzzle #62. Across: 2. cannibal = canibal, 6. pyre = rug, 7. torrid = torid, 8. homesickness = nostalgie, 11. lecherous = libidinos, 13. jocular = comic, 16. tobacconist = tutungiu, 19. minuet = menuet, 21. papyrus = papirus, 23. collectivity = colectivitate, 27. discoverer = descoperitor, 28. mush = terci, 29. minstrel = menestrel, 30. shortness = scurtime. **Down:** 1. pylon = pilon, 3. alum = alaun, 4. purveyor = furnizor, 5. settler = colonist, 9. satchel = ghiozdan, 10. liveliness = vioiciune, 12. steadfast = stabil, 14. annunciation = vestire, 15. entire = total, 17. usurper = uzurpator, 18. disinfectant = dezinfectant, 20. philology = filologie, 22. obsequious = slugarnic, 24. superman = supraom, 25. dwarf = pitic, 26. volleyball = Volei.

Puzzle #63. Across: 2. malleable = maleabil, 5. wanderer = hoinar, 8. adornment = ornament, 10. tannin = tanin, 14. lithography = litografie, 16. bison = bizon, 17. upstart = parvenit, 18. sightless = orb, 26. confection = dulciuri, 27. roundness = rotunjime, 28. pessimist = pesimist, 29. stormy = furtunos. **Down:** 1. freemasonry = francmasonerie, 3. abscess = abces, 4. jester = bufon, 6. quince = Gutuie, 7. inedible = necomestibil, 8. abhorrence = oroare, 9. bivouac = bivuac, 11. midshipman = aspirant, 12. smuggler = contrabandist, 13. udder = uger, 15. turnip = nap, 19. asunder = separat, 20. mortification = umilire, 21. brisk = vioi, 22. bookish = livresc, 23. zealot = fanatic, 24. typhoon = taifun, 25. ferrous = feros.

Puzzle #64. Across: 5. collectivization = colectivizare, 6. skunk = sconcs, 9. wart = neg, 12. effusion = efuziune, 13. haughty = arogant, 15. nonentity = nulitate, 16. adieu = adio, 17. bartender = Barman, 20. engraver = gravor, 26. dustman = gunoier, 27. deserter = dezertor, 28. skilful = priceput, 29. hypodermic = subcutanat, 30. projectile = proiectil. **Down:** 1. acme = culme, 2. cyst = chist, 3. rumpus = scandal, 4. vagrancy = vagabondaj, 7. tiresome = obositor, 8. satyr = satir, 10. glazier = geamgiu, 11.

aphorism = aforism, 14. turbid = tulbure, 18. troubadour = trubadur, 19. excerpt = fragment, 21. technologist = tehnolog, 22. gnarled = noduros, 23. stationer = papetar, 24. drinkable = potabil, 25. suet = seu.

Puzzle #65. Across: 1. mannerism = manierism, 4. hornet = viespe, 5. inequity = nedreptate, 7. ticklish = dificil, 8. pomegranate = rodie, 10. speedometer = vitezometru, 11. janitor = portar, 12. manikin = manechin, 14. cur = potaie, 15. welder = Sudor, 16. northerner = nordic, 20. skiff = schif, 22. seemly = decent, 24. italic = cursiv, 26. equilateral = echilateral, 27. titter = chicot, 28. sad = trist. **Down:** 2. superhuman = supraomenesc, 3. inattentive = neatent, 5. untiring = neobosit, 6. diphthong = diftong, 9. fop = filfizon, 13. tassel = ciucure, 15. sentient = sensibil, 17. elocution = oratorie, 18. honeyed = mieros, 19. anthracite = antracit, 21. guffaw = hohot, 23. hurrah = ura, 25. isthmus = istm.

Puzzle #66. Across: 3. wheelwright = rotar, 5. baccy = tabac, 7. camphor = camfor, 8. polygamy = poligamie, 10. wrecker = diversionist, 11. ruffian = bandit, 16. zephyr = zefir, 17. cock = cocoş, 19. piteous = jalnic, 24. dahlia = dalie, 25. tomcat = motan, 27. swordsman = spadasin, 28. juggler = jongler, 29. aesthete = estet, 30. bawl = zbieret. **Down:** 1. physiognomy = fizionomie, 2. bagpipe = cimpoi, 4. tympanum = timpan, 6. confectioner = cofetar, 9. xylophone = xilofon, 12. vapid = insipid, 13. bloodhound = copoi, 14. dysentery = dizenterie, 15. rickets = rahitism, 18. overwrought = surescitat, 20. slanderous = calomnios, 21. amiability = amabilitate, 22. boomerang = bumerang, 23. lentil = linte, 26. peppery = piperat.

Puzzle #67. Across: 5. humorist = umorist, 8. lackey = lacheu, 10. warble = ciripit, 12. mumps = oreion, 13. blackleg = escroc, 15. alembic = alambic, 16. annular = inelar, 18. gimlet = sfredel, 22. trousseau = trusou, 23. neuralgia = nevralgie, 24. sweetish = dulceag, 26. gymnast = gimnast, 27. truant = chiulangiu, 28. anthrax = dalac, 29. syllogism = silogism. **Down:** 1. jewelry = Bijuterii, 2. scurvy = scorbut, 3. sympathizer = simpatizant, 4. pharynx = faringe, 6. mourner = bocitoare, 7. peony = bujor, 9. docker = docher, 11. polyglot = poliglot, 14. muffler = fular, 15. ammeter = ampermetru, 17. pardonable = scuzabil, 19. haberdashery = mercerie, 20. assiduity = asiduitate, 21. obsequies = funeralii, 25. billow = talaz.

Puzzle #68. Across: 3. embezzlement = delapidare, 5. gusset = clin, 6. freckle = pistrui, 8. vermicelli = fidea, 12. philately = filatelie, 13. quadruped = patruped, 14. freemason = francmason, 15. hydrate = hidrat, 16. exigent = urgent, 17. brassiere = Sutien, 21. wordiness = prolixitate, 23. kerchief = batic, 25. gluey = lipicios, 26. mesmerism = hipnotism, 29. archaism = arhaism, 30. skittle = popic. **Down:** 1. tripper = excursionist, 2. acclimation = aclimatizare, 4. factitious = artificial, 7. illiterate = analfabet, 9. quadrille = cadril, 10. unpractical = nepractic, 11. underfed = subnutrit, 18. tare = dara, 19. impolite = nepoliticos, 20. penmanship = caligrafie, 22. homonym = omonim, 24. ingot = lingou, 27. billion = Miliard, 28. wisecrack = banc.

Puzzle #69. Across: 2. maidenhood = virginitate, 4. afflux = aflux, 5. skeptic = sceptic, 8. hydrate = hidrat, 9. addle = stricat, 11. polygamist = poligam, 14. larboard = babord, 17. millenary = milenar, 18. quintal = chintal, 20. atomizer = pulverizator, 22. dromedary = dromader, 23. romanticist = romantic, 25. dative = dativ, 27. agronomy = agronomie, 28. seraph = serafim, 29. appetizer = Aperitiv. **Down:** 1. pajamas = pijama, 3. embezzlement = delapidare, 6. carousal = chef, 7. cello = violoncel, 10. gulf = golf, 12. acclimation = aclimatizare, 13. pennon = fanion, 14. bigamist = bigam, 15. ampleness = amploare, 16. billion = Miliard, 19. neurasthenia = neurastenie, 21. dactyl = dactil, 24. arch = Arc, 26. tare = dara.

Puzzle #70. Across: 3. atomizer = pulverizator, 4. pajamas = pijama, 9. philately = filatelie, 10. maidenhood = virginitate, 14. hexameter = hexametru, 18. tripper = excursionist, 19. archaism = arhaism, 20. quintal = chintal, 23. vermicelli = fidea, 24. mesmerism = hipnotism, 26. quadruped = patruped, 27. exigent = urgent, 28. parasite = parazit, 29. somnambulist = somnambul, 30. afflux = aflux. **Down:** 1. breviary = breviar, 2. penmanship = caligrafie, 5. millenary = milenar, 6. pennon = fanion, 7. wordiness = prolixitate, 8. wisecrack = banc, 11. factitious = artificial, 12. larboard = babord, 13. kerchief = batic, 15. antonym = antonim, 16. sentimentalist = sentimental, 17. mulatto = mulatru, 21. ingot = lingou, 22. carousal = chef, 25. quadrille = cadril.

Puzzle #71. Across: 3. gimlet = sfredel, 4. homonym = omonim, 5. sweetish = dulceag, 9. skittle = popic, 10. suzerain = suzeran, 13. gluey = lipicios, 15. blackleg = escroc, 20. decease = deces, 22. onomatopoeia = onomatopee, 23. jewelry = Bijuterii, 24. assiduity = asiduitate, 25. precocity = precocitate, 27. beatitude = beatitudine, 28. faucet = Robinet, 29. freemason = francmason. **Down:** 1. petunia = petunie, 2. beefsteak = biftec, 6. vaporous = vaporos, 7. profiteer = profitor, 8. impolite = nepoliticos, 10. underfed = subnutrit, 11. alembic = alambic, 12. infamy = infamie, 14. preponderant = preponderent, 16. freckle = pistrui, 17. exportation = exportare, 18. illiterate = analfabet, 19. unpractical = nepractic, 21. brassiere = Sutien, 26. gusset = clin.

Puzzle #72. Across: 1. benighted = ignorant, 5. purgative = purgativ, 7. mourner = bocitoare, 10. demagogy = demagogie, 12. lackey = lacheu, 13. polyglot = poliglot, 15. beefsteak = biftec, 18. muffler = fular, 19. warble = ciripit, 20. monorail = Monorai, 21. avidity = aviditate, 25. cordiality = cordialitate, 26. obsequies = funeralii, 27. sympathizer = simpatizant, 28. gymnast = gimnast, 29. truant = chiulangiu. **Down:** 2. billow = talaz, 3. bigamy = bigamie, 4. grammarian = gramatician, 6. humorist = umorist, 8. insensibility = insensibilitate, 9. lexicography = lexicografie, 10. anthrax = dalac, 11. syllogism = silogism, 14. indisposed = indispus, 16. parallelogram = paralelogram, 17. cadaverous = cadaveric, 22. prefab = prefabricat, 23. genitive = genitiv, 24. pardonable = scuzabil.

Puzzle #73. Across: 2. haberdashery = mercerie, 5. antipathetic = antipatic, 8. ruffian = bandit, 10. scurvy = scorbut, 11. mumps = oreion, 16. paroxysm = paroxism, 17. participle = participiu, 21. strontium = stronțiu, 22. neuralgia = nevralgie, 23. zephyr = zefir, 25. slanderous = calomnios, 26. perfidious = perfid, 28. docker = docher, 29. vigour = vigoare, 30. trousseau = trusou. **Down:** 1. pharynx = faringe, 3. aesthete = estet, 4. vermouth = vermut, 6. annular = inelar, 7. peony = bujor, 9. libertine = libertin, 12. iridium = iridiu, 13. cock = cocoș, 14. bagpipe = cimpoi, 15. tympanum = timpan, 18. ammeter = ampermetru, 19. stenographer = stenograf, 20. demagogue = demagog, 24. festoon = feston, 27. polecat = dihor.

Puzzle #74. Across: 1. obscene = obscen, 3. baccy = tabac, 5. asperity = asperitate, 7. carmine = carmin, 8. bawl = zbieret, 11. physiognomy = fizionomie, 13. periscope = periscop, 16. conjugation = conjugare, 17. telegraphy = telegrafie, 20. trigonometry = trigonometrie, 23. wrecker = diversionist, 25. bloodhound = copoi, 26. tomcat = motan, 27. confectioner = cofetar, 28. polygamy = poligamie, 29. dahlia = dalie. **Down:** 2. swordsman = spadasin, 4. amiability = amabilitate, 6. wheelwright = rotar, 9. boomerang = bumerang, 10. lentil = linte, 12. artichoke = anghinare, 14. camphor = camfor, 15. peppery = piperat, 16. cataclysm = cataclism, 18. rickets = rahitism, 19. xylophone = xilofon, 21. juggler = jongler, 22. sled = sanie, 24. vapid = insipid.

Puzzle #75. Across: 1. ventricle = ventricul, 5. honeyed = mieros, 7. pomegranate = rodie, 9. manikin = manechin, 10. intransitive = intranzitiv, 13. skiff = schif, 16. overwrought = surescitat, 21. seemly = decent, 22. caprice = capriciu, 24. piteous = jalnic, 25. guffaw = hohot, 27. elocution = oratorie, 28. northerner = nordic, 29. retroactive = retroactiv, 30. dysentery = dizenterie. **Down:** 2. convexity = convexitate, 3. cur = potaie, 4. ticklish = dificil, 6. spore = spor, 8. sled = Sanie, 11. untiring = neobosit, 12. speedometer = vitezometru, 14. scruple = scrupul, 15. tassel = ciucure, 17. titter = chicot, 18. tricolour = tricolor, 19. indissoluble = indisolubil, 20. fop = filfizon, 23. anarchism = anarhism, 26. janitor = portar.

Puzzle #76. Across: 2. sentient = sensibil, 4. debility = debilitate, 6. determinative = determinant, 9. harpoon = harpon, 12. silo = siloz, 14. inattentive = neatent, 16. italic = cursiv, 19. hurrah = ura, 21. stiletto = stilet, 24. megaphone = Megafon, 25. superhuman = supraomenesc, 26. neglectful = neglijent, 28. mannerism = manierism, 29. anthracite = antracit. **Down:** 1. welder = Sudor, 3. banality = banalitate, 5. antimony = antimoniu, 7. microbe = microb, 8. sad = trist, 10. hornet = viespe, 11. hippopotamus = Hipopotam, 13. pariah = paria, 14. inequity = nedreptate, 15. laureate = laureat, 17. interrogative = interogativ, 18. equilateral = echilateral, 20. diphthong = diftong, 22. credulous = credul, 23. semicircle = semicerc, 27. isthmus = istm.

Puzzle #77. Across: 1. excerpt = fragment, 5. stationer = papetar, 7. nonentity = nulitate, 10. tiresome = obositor, 11. convulsion = convulsie, 13. voltmeter = voltmetru, 16. dustman = gunoier, 18. incorruptible = incoruptibil, 25. collectivization = colectivizare, 26. sardine = sardea, 27. technologist = tehnolog, 28. trapeze = trapez, 29. deserter = dezertor, 30. glazier = geamgiu. **Down:** 2. effusion = efuziune, 3. drinkable = potabil, 4. acme = culme, 6. adieu = adio, 8. lascivious = lasciv, 9. ostracism = ostracizare, 12. suet = seu, 14. projectile = proiectil, 15. paralytic = paralitic, 17. wart = neg, 19. skunk = sconcs, 20. rumpus = scandal, 21. vagrancy = vagabondaj, 22. pedantry = pedanterie, 23. turbid = tulbure, 24. semester = semestru.

Puzzle #78. Across: 1. freemasonry = francmasonerie, 6. engraver = gravor, 7. macaroni = macaroane, 9. bartender = Barman, 12. satyr = satir, 13. cyst = chist, 14. menagerie = menajerie, 15. pessimist = pesimist, 17. turnip = nap, 21. voluble = volubil, 23. neurology = neurologie, 24. abacus = abac, 25. notary = notar, 26. quince = Gutuie, 28. abscess = abces, 29. skilful = priceput. **Down:** 2. haughty = arogant, 3. gnarled = noduros, 4. brisk = vioi, 5. monotheism = monoteism, 8. aphorism = aforism, 9. suspenders = bretele, 10. lithography = litografie, 11. roundness = rotunjime, 16. hypodermic = subcutanat, 18. mortification = umilire, 19. trill = tril, 20. troubadour = trubadur, 22. sightless = orb, 27. udder = uger.

Puzzle #79. Across: 2. smuggler = contrabandist, 5. etymology = etimologie, 8. combustible = combustibil, 9. plagiarism = plagiat, 15. bivouac = bivuac, 16. inedible = necomestibil, 17. abhorrence = oroare, 20. louse = păduche, 21. orifice = orificiu, 22. monocle = monoclu, 24. albatross = albatros, 26. sacrilege = sacrilegiu, 28. asunder = separat, 29. melodious = melodios, 30. ferrous = feros. **Down:** 1. ductile = ductil, 3. confection = dulciuri, 4. stormy = furtunos, 6. tannin = tanin, 7. midshipman = aspirant, 10. amethyst = ametist, 11. zealot = fanatic, 12. timidity = timiditate, 13. malleable = maleabil, 14. rapacious = rapace, 18. sedative = sedativ, 19. adornment = ornament, 23. bookish = livresc, 25. bison = bizon, 27. colossus = colos.

Puzzle #80. Across: 1. transitive = tranzitiv, 6. impure = impur, 7. upstart = parvenit, 10. steadfast = stabil, 12. ovary = ovar, 13. philology = filologie, 16. basement = subsol, 17. jester = bufon, 18. monolith = monolit, 21. apogee = apogeu, 23. superlative = superlativ, 25. alchemist = alchimist, 26. recitation = recitare, 27. torrid = torid, 28. cannibal = canibal. **Down:** 2. isosceles = isoscel, 3. alum = alaun, 4. starling = graur, 5. biplane = biplan, 6. inflammable = inflamabil, 8. liveliness = vioiciune, 9. sonorous = sonor, 11. typhoon = taifun, 14. plebiscite = plebiscit, 15. wanderer = hoinar, 16. superman = supraom, 19. interstate = interstatal, 20. semaphore = semafor, 22. optimistic = optimist, 24. annunciation = vestire.

Puzzle #81. Across: 1. zoologist = zoolog, 3. excess = exces, 9. minuet = menuet, 10. telepathy = telepatie, 12. papyrus = papirus, 14. hammock = hamac, 19. metallurgy = metalurgie, 22. elegy = elegie, 23. ladle = polonic, 24. dwarf = pitic, 26. pyre = rug, 28. irascible = irascibil, 29. lignite = lignit, 30. mineralogy = mineralogie. **Down:** 2. tulip = Lalea, 4. collectivity = colectivitate,

5. strategist = strateg, 6. sterility = sterilitate, 7. tobacconist = tutungiu, 8. purveyor = furnizor, 11. homesickness = nostalgie, 13. planter = plantator, 15. usurper = uzurpator, 16. subterfuge = subterfugiu, 17. disinfectant = dezinfectant, 18. centigrade = centigrad, 20. idolatry = idolatrie, 21. zipper = fermoar, 25. epilogue = epilog, 27. pylon = pilon.

Puzzle #82. Across: 2. settler = colonist, 5. alligator = Aligator, 7. paternity = paternitate, 10. invader = invadator, 11. mush = terci, 12. satchel = ghiozdan, 13. trombone = trombon, 14. lecherous = libidinos, 17. obsequious = slugarnic, 19. storehouse = depozit, 20. sanatorium = sanatoriu, 24. throaty = gutural, 26. inalienable = inalienabil, 27. shortness = scurtime, 29. sectarianism = sectarism, 30. smallness = micime. **Down:** 1. jocular = comic, 3. impressionism = impresionism, 4. kayak = Caiac, 6. lucidity = luciditate, 8. emissary = emisar, 9. discoverer = descoperitor, 15. monstrosity = monstruozitate, 16. fillip = stimulent, 18. repulsion = repulsie, 21. scurrilous = injurios, 22. minstrel = menestrel, 23. volleyball = Volei, 25. studious = studios, 28. entire = total.

Puzzle #83. Across: 6. fatality = calamitate, 8. monologue = monolog, 9. saxophone = saxofon, 10. shrew = scorpie, 12. trachea = trahee, 13. ochre = ocru, 14. jaundice = icter, 16. abstruse = ascuns, 18. cyclone = ciclon, 25. virility = virilitate, 26. penknife = briceag, 28. meteorite = meteorit, 29. microbiology = microbiologie, 30. perforation = perforare. **Down:** 1. protractor = raportor, 2. cynic = cinic, 3. belligerent = beligerant, 4. breakwater = dig, 5. inoculation = inoculare, 7. laziness = lene, 11. depravity = depravare, 15. shipwreck = Naufragiu, 17. portly = corpolent, 19. insincere = nesincer, 20. perversity = perversitate, 21. fingernail = unghie, 22. prolongation = prelungire, 23. servitude = robie, 24. stethoscope = stetoscop, 27. purr = tors.

Puzzle #84. Across: 1. navigable = navigabil, 5. skier = schior, 7. manger = iesle, 10. inaccuracy = inexactitate, 12. marten = jder, 13. bricklayer = zidar, 15. woodcock = Sitar, 16. pumpkin = Dovleac, 18. shrew = scorpie, 23. iodine = iod, 26. climber = Alpinist, 27. lugubrious = lugubru, 28. tadpole = mormoloc, 29. recitative = recitativ. **Down:** 2. lamentable = lamentabil, 3. divisible = divizibil, 4. renown = renume, 5. preternatural = supranatural, 6. hilarity = ilaritate, 8. pollination = polenizare, 9. locket = medalion, 11. tyrannical = tiranic, 14. demonstrative = demonstrativ, 17. adorable = adorabil, 19. harbor = Port, 20. syllabic = silabic, 21. fireman = Fochist, 22. baritone = bariton, 24. leper = lepros, 25. aircraft = avion.

Puzzle #85. Across: 2. python = piton, 4. vagrant = vagabond, 6. zeppelin = Zepelin, 8. obtuse = obtuz, 11. larynx = laringe, 13. equestrian = ecvestru, 14. woodpecker = ciocănitoare, 15. aircraft = avion, 17. mildew = mucegai, 21. rabid = turbat, 23. morose = ursuz, 24. expressionism = expresionism, 26. epithet = epitet, 27. impresario = impresar, 28. behavior = purtare, 29. auspicious = favorabil, 30. tailoring = croitorie. **Down:** 1. demonstrator = manifestant, 3. incision = incizie, 5. diametrically = diametral, 7. extermination = exterminare, 9. thermos = termos, 10. thrifty = econom, 12. excommunication = excomunicare, 16. greengrocer = zarzavagiu, 18. crusader = cruciat, 19. whey = zer, 20. sewerage = canalizare, 22. corkscrew = tirbuşon, 25. eucalyptus = eucalipt.

Puzzle #86. Across: 1. asterisk = asterisc, 3. dynamo = dinam, 4. prodigal = risipitor, 6. confessor = duhovnic, 9. xenophobia = xenofobie, 12. invocation = invocare, 14. accordion = acordeon, 17. virtuosity = virtuozitate, 18. boatman = barcagiu, 20. indivisible = indivizibil, 23. tributary = afluent, 25. alchemy = alchimie, 26. ephemeral = efemer, 27. rabies = turbare, 28. slave = sclav. **Down:** 1. amphibious = amfibiu, 2. onlooker = spectator, 5. poodle = pudel, 7. odyssey = odisee, 8. apostrophe = apostrof, 10. staid = serios, 11. scooter = scuter, 13. asphalt = asfalt, 15. stilts = catalige, 16. anchoret = pustnic, 19. renegade = renegat, 21. greedy = lacom, 22. sheepish = timid, 23. azure = azur, 24. tonnage = tonaj.

Puzzle #87. Across: 1. chandelier = candelabru, 3. horned = cornut, 5. spindle = fus, 8. zoology = zoologie, 11. atheism = ateism, 13. counterpoint = contrapunct, 15. nebulous = nebulos, 17. scholastic = scolastic, 19. liqueur = lichior, 22. downcast = deprimat, 23. asperity = asprime, 24. pseudonym = pseudonim, 26. fission = fisiune, 28. balm = balsam, 29. cloudless = senin, 30. deformity = diformitate. **Down:** 2. ecstasy = extaz, 4. bureaucrat = birocrat, 6. sprinkler = stropitoare, 7. oblique = oblic, 9. staid = serios, 10. solemnity = solemnitate, 12. euphemism = eufemism, 14. nothingness = nimicnicie, 16. pulley = scripete, 18. fickle = capricios, 20. predicative = predicativ, 21. propulsion = propulsie, 25. layman = profan, 27. virile = viril.

Puzzle #88. Across: 3. itinerant = ambulant, 4. lapel = rever, 9. pus = puroi, 10. oboe = oboi, 14. vulgarity = vulgaritate, 15. totalitarian = totalitar, 17. courtier = curtean, 18. mediocrity = mediocritate, 20. encyclopedia = Enciclopedie, 22. patrimony = patrimoniu, 23. fanaticism = fanatism, 25. longitude = longitudine, 27. opportunism = oportunism, 28. basalt = bazalt, 29. coachman = vizitiu. **Down:** 1. oligarchy = oligarhie, 2. parody = parodie, 5. preconceived = preconceput, 6. manganese = mangan, 7. fiend = diavol, 8. innkeeper = hangiu, 11. ostentatious = ostentativ, 12. imperceptible = imperceptibil, 13. peculiarity = particularitate, 16. couplet = cuplet, 19. docile = docil, 21. unobserved = neobservat, 24. airman = aviator, 26. delirium = delir, 27. odious = odios.

Puzzle #89. Across: 6. ponderous = greoi, 8. ammonium = amoniu, 9. celluloid = celuloid, 10. starch = amidon, 11. fluff = puf, 12. asparagus = sparanghel, 15. ethereal = eteric, 16. apparition = vedenie, 17. utopia = utopie, 19. incoherent = incoerent, 22. voluptuous = voluptos, 23. pert = obraznic, 24. mercenary = mercenar, 26. sorrel = Roib, 27. precocious = precoce, 28. harlequin = arlechin, 29. affable = amabil, 30. quizzical = ironic. **Down:** 1. kaleidoscope = caleidoscop, 2. barbarian = barbar,

3. diminutive = diminutiv, 4. flirtation = flirt, 5. artful = viclean, 7. rhinoceros = rinocer, 13. spaniel = prepelicar, 14. inhabitant = locuitor, 18. irreducible = ireductibil, 20. ointment = alifie, 21. flabby = flasc, 25. chromium = crom.

Puzzle #90. Across: 2. mirage = miraj, 5. greenish = verzui, 6. chaste = cast, 7. genocide = genocid, 9. autopsy = autopsie, 11. amphitheatre = amfiteatru, 16. pattern = model, 17. kangaroo = Cangur, 19. calculation = calcul, 21. unremitting = perseverent, 22. vampire = vampir, 24. narration = relatare, 25. stalwart = robust, 26. rheumatism = reumatism, 27. consulate = consulat. **Down:** 1. proletarian = proletar, 2. prodigy = minune, 3. migratory = migrator, 4. nickel = nichel, 5. vassal = vasal, 8. dictation = dictare, 10. leek = praz, 12. imperious = imperios, 13. derogatory = peiorativ, 14. mediaeval = medieval, 15. indistinct = neclar, 17. color = Culoare, 18. heredity = ereditate, 20. sapphire = safir, 23. ostrich = struţ.

Puzzle #91. Across: 2. trowel = mistrie, 4. tripod = Trepied, 5. quits = chit, 8. elliptical = eliptic, 13. purgatory = purgatoriu, 14. leech = lipitoare, 16. grapefruit = Grepfrut, 19. concave = concav, 20. irregularity = neregularitate, 21. outcast = proscris, 23. plaid = Pled, 24. jasmine = iasomie, 26. succinct = succint, 27. canine = canin, 28. perfunctory = superficial. **Down:** 1. uninhabited = nelocuit, 3. electrode = electrod, 6. foray = incursiune, 7. fastidious = mofturos, 9. millet = mei, 10. sucker = sugar, 11. pallor = paloare, 12. venereal = veneric, 15. tenacious = tenace, 17. thermostat = termostat, 18. informer = informator, 19. cypress = Chiparos, 21. passive = pasiv, 22. benzene = benzen, 25. gaseous = gazos.

Puzzle #92. Across: 1. harpsichord = clavecin, 5. lethargy = letargie, 8. purposely = dinadins, 10. brevity = concizie, 12. poplar = plop, 13. nobleman = nobil, 15. epitaph = epitaf, 19. surrealism = suprarealism, 20. chastity = castitate, 24. hurricane = uragan, 26. hospitable = ospitalier, 27. billion = Bilion, 28. heroism = eroism, 29. cowardice = laşitate. **Down:** 2. motley = amestecat, 3. feline = felin, 4. pathos = patos, 6. pang = junghi, 7. acne = acnee, 9. nitric = azotic, 11. snobbery = snobism, 12. slipper = papuc, 14. disorderly = turbulent, 16. trilogy = trilogie, 17. shoemaker = cizmar, 18. atrocious = atroce, 21. synonym = sinonim, 22. navel = buric, 23. movable = mobil, 25. fibrous = fibros.

Puzzle #93. Across: 1. drugstore = Farmacie, 5. beaver = castor, 7. adventurer = aventurier, 9. opportunist = oportunist, 11. avoidable = evitabil, 13. custodian = custode, 17. piracy = piraterie, 18. posthumous = postum, 21. indigestion = Indigestie, 23. snout = bot, 24. blizzard = viscol, 25. furrow = rid, 28. typist = dactilograf, 29. disciple = discipol, 30. suffix = sufix. **Down:** 2. hypocrite = ipocrit, 3. concise = concis, 4. shutter = oblon, 6. conqueror = cuceritor, 8. bearable = suportabil, 10. incurable = incurabil, 12. venomous = veninos, 14. enormity = enormitate, 15. astrology = astrologie, 16. archipelago = arhipelag, 19. monsoon = muson, 20. raven = corb, 22. virtuoso = virtuos, 26. unfaithful = infidel, 27. gait = mers.

Puzzle #94. Across: 1. mystic = mistic, 6. irrevocable = irevocabil, 9. zoological = zoologic, 11. pedagogy = pedagogie, 14. subway = metrou, 15. nakedness = goliciune, 17. delinquent = delincvent, 18. supposition = presupunere, 21. palpable = palpabil, 22. ether = eter, 24. reprisals = represalii, 25. slime = noroi, 27. watchman = paznic, 28. fragility = fragilitate, 29. scrupulous = scrupulos, 30. medley = amestec. **Down:** 2. spinach = spanac, 3. orgy = orgie, 4. barter = troc, 5. disorderly = dezordonat, 7. reverie = visare, 8. distillation = distilare, 10. laurel = laur, 12. nudge = ghiont, 13. degeneration = degenerare, 16. nautical = nautic, 19. rationalism = raţionalism, 20. wad = tampon, 23. astronomer = astronom, 26. crane = macara.

Puzzle #95. Across: 1. preposterous = absurd, 3. mauve = mov, 7. immorality = imoralitate, 8. bridegroom = mire, 15. layer = strat, 16. submissive = supus, 18. artisan = artizan, 19. predicate = predicat, 22. propeller = Elice, 23. thistle = ciulin, 26. constabulary = jandarmerie, 27. categorical = categoric, 29. incapacity = incapacitate. **Down:** 2. solidity = soliditate, 4. voluminous = voluminos, 5. patriarch = patriarh, 6. reciprocity = reciprocitate, 9. teller = povestitor, 10. sedentary = sedentar, 11. encore = bis, 12. thermometer = termometru, 13. blasphemy = blasfemie, 14. equatorial = ecuatorial, 17. wistful = melancolic, 19. averse = potrivnic, 20. dowry = zestre, 21. methodical = metodic, 24. seduction = farmec, 25. figurative = figurat, 28. reindeer = ren.

Puzzle #96. Across: 4. infallible = infailibil, 7. homicide = omucidere, 10. chimpanzee = cimpanzeu, 11. penniless = lefter, 12. exertion = exercitare, 17. desertion = dezertare, 20. sonnet = sonet, 21. ebony = abanos, 22. trump = atu, 23. barometer = barometru, 26. shroud = giulgiu, 27. porous = poros, 28. perceptible = perceptibil, 29. assignee = cesionar, 30. linguist = lingvist. **Down:** 1. allusion = aluzie, 2. thorny = spinos, 3. forked = bifurcat, 5. inactivity = inactivitate, 6. cashier = casier, 8. mascara = rimel, 9. accessory = accesoriu, 13. cedar = cedru, 14. iceberg = Aisberg, 15. uterus = uter, 16. monotony = monotonie, 18. eel = ţipar, 19. transverse = transversal, 24. prologue = prolog, 25. thyme = cimbru.

Puzzle #97. Across: 5. veneer = furnir, 6. sanitation = salubritate, 12. soot = funingine, 13. passivity = pasivitate, 14. waltz = vals, 17. trajectory = traiectorie, 19. plywood = placaj, 20. flea = purice, 21. gunner = tunar, 23. mime = mim, 24. annals = anale, 25. ruddy = rumen, 27. gaiety = veselie, 28. bazaar = bazar, 29. monograph = monografie. **Down:** 1. axle = osie, 2. autograph = autograf, 3. gable = fronton, 4. humanism = umanism, 7. utopian = utopic, 8. sparrow = vrabie, 9. unprofitable = nerentabil, 10. vanilla = vanilie, 11. apostle = apostol, 12. bankrupt = falit, 15. orphan = orfan, 16. unbalanced = dezechilibrat, 18. conceivable = imaginabil, 22. romanticism = romantism, 26. lobe = lob.

Puzzle #98. Across: 2. nightingale = privighetoare, 7. interlude = interludiu, 8. glossary = glosar, 9. diver = scafandru, 15. evaporation = evaporare, 17. curious = curios, 20. theorist = teoretician, 26. impassable = impracticabil, 28. inexorable =

implacabil, 29. psychiatry = psihiatrie, 30. inferiority = inferioritate. **Down:** 1. oppressor = tiran, 3. mediocre = mediocru, 4. feverish = febril, 5. contagious = contagios, 6. poppy = mac, 10. antipathy = antipatie, 11. mysticism = misticism, 12. deafness = surzenie, 13. pilgrim = pelerin, 14. noxious = nociv, 16. roe = Icre, 18. lowly = modest, 19. cosmopolitan = cosmopolit, 21. utilitarian = utilitar, 22. discount = Rabat, 23. radish = Ridiche, 24. wick = Fitil, 25. phosphorus = fosfor, 27. zenith = zenit.

Puzzle #99. Across: 4. howl = urlet, 7. accomplice = complice, 11. antidote = antidot, 14. canonical = canonic, 15. repertory = repertoriu, 17. pessimism = pesimism, 23. honest = cinstit, 24. robber = jefuitor, 26. sanitary = igienic, 27. starboard = tribord, 28. posterity = posteritate. **Down:** 1. biologist = biolog, 2. orphanage = orfelinat, 3. beige = bej, 5. disinterested = dezinteresat, 6. unanimity = unanimitate, 8. isotope = izotop, 9. clandestine = clandestin, 10. fad = manie, 12. sundry = divers, 13. impassive = impasibil, 14. quartz = cuarț, 16. sectarian = sectar, 17. wren = Pitulice, 18. squalor = mizerie, 19. senile = senil, 20. weighty = important, 21. sociable = sociabil, 22. hectare = hectar, 25. vineyard = vie.

Puzzle #100. Across: 3. deacon = diacon, 6. harmless = inofensiv, 7. venerable = venerabil, 8. conical = conic, 9. spherical = sferic, 11. graphite = grafit, 13. glassy = sticlos, 17. phoneme = fonem, 19. allegory = alegorie, 20. cylindrical = cilindric, 24. envious = invidios, 25. immoral = imoral, 26. equator = ecuator, 27. ox = bou, 28. aptitude = aptitudine, 29. anthology = antologie, 30. labyrinth = labirint. **Down:** 1. humanist = umanist, 2. clover = trifoi, 4. copious = abundent, 5. biochemistry = biochimie, 10. projector = proiector, 12. melon = Pepene, 14. espionage = spionaj, 15. reformer = reformator, 16. sportsman = sportiv, 18. boulevard = Bulevard, 21. convocation = convocare, 22. pedestal = piedestal, 23. casino = Cazinou.